SONSENSE NONGS

Michael Rosen's book of silly songs, daft ditties, crazy croons,
loony lyrics, batty ballads and nutty numbers

Chosen by Michael Rosen
with illustrations by Shoo Rayner

A & C Black • London

First published in 1992 by A & C Black (Publishers) Ltd
35 Bedford Row, London WC1R 4JH

Reprinted 1994
Illustrations © 1992 by Shoo Rayner
Designer: Michael Leaman
Editor: Sheena Roberts
Typeset by Seton Music Graphics Ltd, Eire
Printed in Great Britain by Hollen Street Press, Berwick upon Tweed

ISBN 0 7136 3557 6

Contents

For silly little ones

Made of plastic

Whoppers

Mumbololo jumbololo

Barmy beasts

Round the bend

Horrors

Scoff

Family album

Hasten, hasten, fetch a basin

What a way to go

1 Throw it out the window

Traditional

Mary had a little lamb,
Its fleece was white as snow,
And everywhere that Mary went
She threw it out the window.
  The window, the window,
  The second storey window,
  And everywhere that Mary went
  She threw it out the window.

Old Mother Hubbard went to the cupboard
To fetch her poor dog a bone,
But when she got there, the cupboard was bare
So she threw it out the window.
  The window, the window,
  The second storey window,
  But when she got there, the cupboard was bare,
  So she threw it out the window.

The grand old Duke of York
He had ten thousand men,
He marched them up to the top of the hill
And threw them out the window ...

Yankee Doodle came to town,
Riding on a pony,
He stuck a feather in his hat
And threw it out the window ...

How many more nursery rhyme characters can you throw out the window?

Silly sounds: *add on a* ***groundshaker*** *at the end of each chorus.*

2 One man went to mow

Traditional; this version collected by Nancy Kerr

One man went to mow,
Went to mow a meadow,
One man and his supersonic sausage dog
with rubber suckers on its feet and metal
caps upon its teeth,
Went to mow a meadow.

Two men went to mow,
Went to mow a meadow,
Two men, one man and his supersonic
sausage dog ...

and so on up to ten

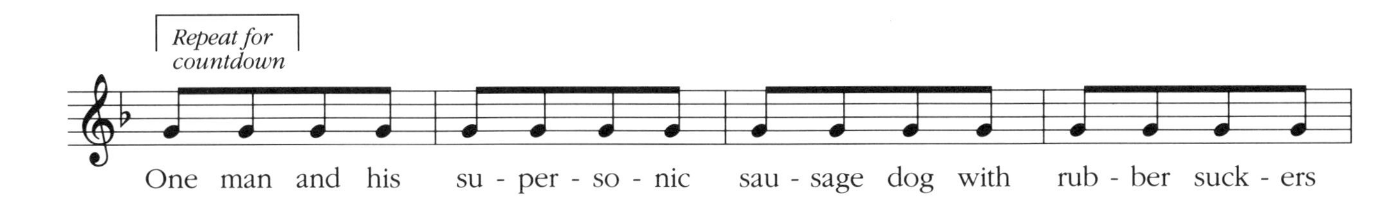

Each time you add a man, add another person, animal or thing to the list.

Silly sounds: supersonic sausage dog – *party whizzer*, rubber suckers – ***underarm squelch***, metal caps on teeth – *squashed drink cans scrubbed together.*

3 Three craws sat upon a wa'

Traditional Scottish

Three craws sat upon a wa',
Sat upon a wa',
Sat upon a wa' - a' - a' - a',
Three craws sat upon a wa'
On a cold and frosty morning.

The first craw couldnae flee at a',
Couldnae flee at a',
Couldnae flee at a' - a' - a' - a',
The first craw couldnae flee at a'
On a cold and frosty morning.

The second craw fell and broke his jaw,
Fell and broke his jaw,
Fell and broke his jaw - aw - aw - aw,
The second craw fell and broke his jaw
On a cold and frosty morning.

The third craw went and told his maw,
Went and told his maw,
Went and told his maw - aw - aw - aw,
The third craw went and told his maw
On a cold and frosty morning.

The fourth craw wisnae there at a',
Wisnae there at a',
Wisnae there at a' - a' - a' - a',
The fourth craw wisnae there at a'
On a cold and frosty morning.

Silly sounds: spineshivers *are good for crow imitations.*

4 Little Rabbit Foo Foo

Traditional; this version collected by Nancy Kerr

Sing:

Little Rabbit Foo Foo,
Skipping through the radishes,
Scooping up all the dormice
And bopping them on the head: BOP!

Down came the Blue Fairy and sang,

'Little Rabbit Foo Foo,
I don't like your attitude,
Scooping up all the dormice
And bopping them on the head: BOP!

Spoken:

'I'll give you three chances;
If you use them all up
I'll turn you into a GOOOOOON!'

But the very next day:

Little Rabbit Foo Foo,
Skipping through the radishes,
Scooping up all the dormice
And bopping them on the head: BOP!

Down came the Blue Fairy and said,

'Little Rabbit Foo Foo,
I don't like your attitude,
Scooping up all the dormice
And bopping them on the head: BOP!

'I gave you three chances;
You've used up one of them,
If you use up the other two chances,
I'll turn you into a GOOOON!'

But the very next day:

Little Rabbit Foo Foo,
Skipping through the radishes ...

Down came the Blue Fairy and said,

'Little Rabbit Foo Foo,
I don't like your attitude ...

I gave you three chances;
You've used up two of them,
If you use up the other chance
I'll turn you into a GOOOON!'

But the very next day:

Little Rabbit Foo Foo,
Skipping through the radishes ...

Down came the Blue Fairy and said,

'Little Rabbit Foo Foo,
I don't like your attitude ...

I gave you three chances,
You've used them all up
And I'm going to turn you into a GOOOON!
POW!

Everyone freezes into a goon

And the moral of the story is:
Hare today, goon tomorrow!

5 The german measles

Traditional English

I had the german measles,
I had them very bad.
They wrapped me in a blanket
And put me in a van.

The van was very bumpy,
I nearly tumbled out,
And when I got to hospital
I heard a baby shout:

'Mamma, dadda, take me home,
From this little rusty home.

I've been here a year or two
And oh I want to stay with you.'

Here comes a doctor, Doctor Brown,
Looking up and looking down.
'Are you ill, or are you not?'
'Yes I am, you silly clot.'

Here comes Doctor Glannister,
Sliding down the bannister.

Halfway down he ripped his pants,
And now he's doing a cha-cha dance.

Da da da da,
Da da da da,
Da da da da ...

6 Five little monkeys

Traditional

Five little monkeys bouncing on the bed,
One fell off and bumped his head.
Mamma called the doctor and the doctor said,
'NO MORE MONKEY BUSINESS BOUNCING
ON THE BED!'

Four little monkeys bouncing on the bed ...

and so on down to one

Silly sounds: headbopper *after* 'bumped his head'.

7 Do your ears hang low?

Traditional

Do your ears hang low?
(Do the actions with your arms)

Do they wobble to and fro?

Can you tie them in a knot?

Can you tie them in a bow?

Can you throw them over your shoulder

Like a regimental soldier?

Do your ears hang low?

Do your ears hang high?

Do they wave up in the sky?

Do they crinkle when they're wet?

Do they straighten when they're dry?

Can you wave them at your neighbour

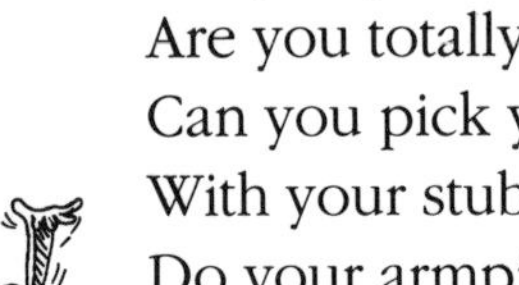

With a minimum of labour?

Do your ears hang high?

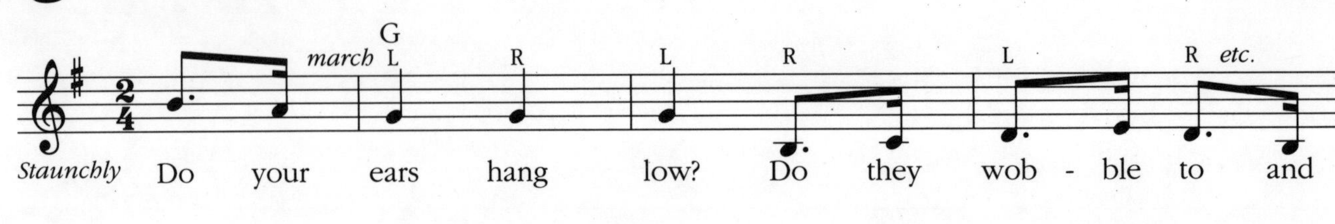

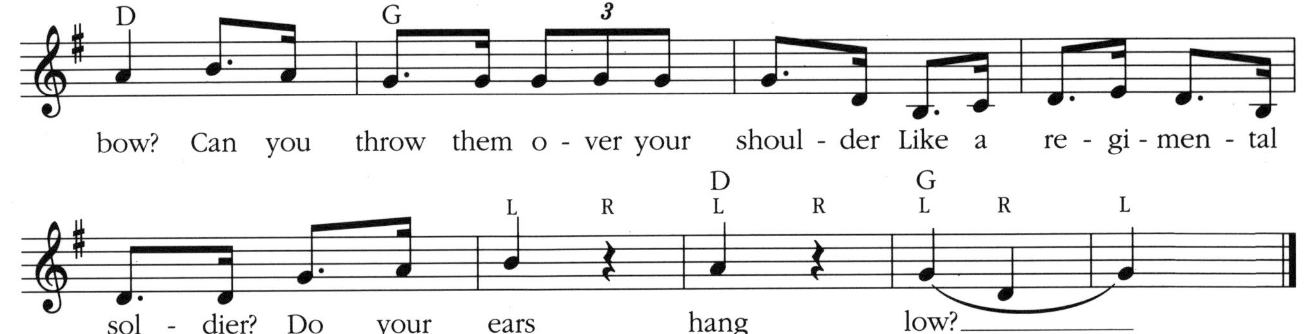

8 Are you pink and green?

Are you pink and green?
Are you totally obscene?
Can you pick your nose
With your stubby little toes?
Do your armpits smell?
Are you hairy there as well?
Do your teeth fall out?

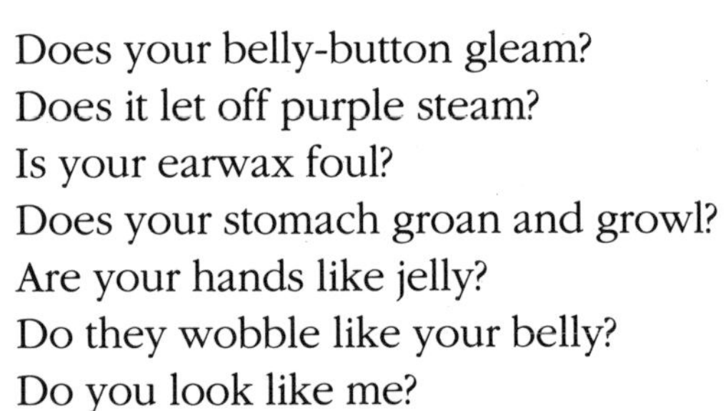

Does your belly-button gleam?
Does it let off purple steam?
Is your earwax foul?
Does your stomach groan and growl?
Are your hands like jelly?
Do they wobble like your belly?
Do you look like me?

Trina Bose, Sara Isenberg, Martina Klich, Rebecca Ryan and Sheetal Borhara, Moss Hall Junior School

9 Joe's got a head like a ping-pong ball

Traditional

Joe's got a head like a ping-pong ball,
Joe's got a head like a ping-pong ball,
Joe's got a head like a ping-pong ball,
ping-pong, ping-pong ball.

Joe's got a head like a ping-pong, ping-pong,
ping-pong, ping-pong, ping-pong ball,
Joe's got a head like a ping-pong, ping-pong,
ping-pong, ping-pong ball.

Joe's got a head like a ping-pong ball,
Joe's got a head like a ping-pong ball,
Joe's got a head like a ping-pong ball,
ping-pong, ping-pong ball.

Silly sounds: cheekpoppers *at random.*

TUNE: *The Lone Ranger*

The Lone Ranger saw Tonto with a dustbin lid on his back,
So he said, 'Why are you wearing that dustbin lid, Tonto?'
And Tonto said (to the tune of The Lone Ranger):

'To the dump, to the dump, to the dump dump dump ...'

10 Something's drastic

Michael Rosen

Group A Something's drastic
Something's drastic
Something's drastic
Something's drastic ...
continue chanting

Group B My ears are elastic

Group B My nose is made of plastic

Group B I'M FANTASTIC!

Group A chants Something's drastic *throughout. Group B mimes dramatically. The whole thing can be repeated. Try getting faster and faster then freeze.*

11 The bathtub song
Traditional
Mother: Michael, where are you going?
Michael: Upstairs to take a bath.
Mother: Michael with legs like toothpicks
All: And a neck like a giraffe.
Michael, into the bathtub,
Pulled out the plug and then –
spoken
Oh, my goodness, oh, my soul,
There goes Michael down the hole!
Mother: Michael, where are you going?
sing into cupped hands
Michael: Downstairs, inside the drain.
Mother: Simon, go catch your brother,
All: He's slipping out again.
Simon: Mother, I caught my brother,
Pulled him out of the drain –
spoken - hold nose for nasal effect
All: Oh, my goodness, oh my dear,
What's that smell of skunk round here.
Mother: Michael, where are you going ...
Lugubriously
C
Mi - chael, where are you go - ing? Up - stairs to take a
G
bath. Mi - chael with legs like tooth - picks And a
C
Fine
neck like a gi - raffe. Mi - chael, in - to the
G
bath - tub, Pulled out the plug and then:
D.C.
Oh my good - ness, oh my soul, there goes Mi - chael down the hole.

12 Tall straw hat

Words: Chris Green Melody: French

Tall straw hat, short straw hat - wide brim,
Short straw hat, tall straw hat - narrow brim,
Tall straw hat with bows - wide brim,
Short straw hat with bows - narrow brim.

Sing it twice. The first time do the actions as shown. The second time do the opposite action for tall, short, wide *and* narrow. *Try doing it really quickly.*

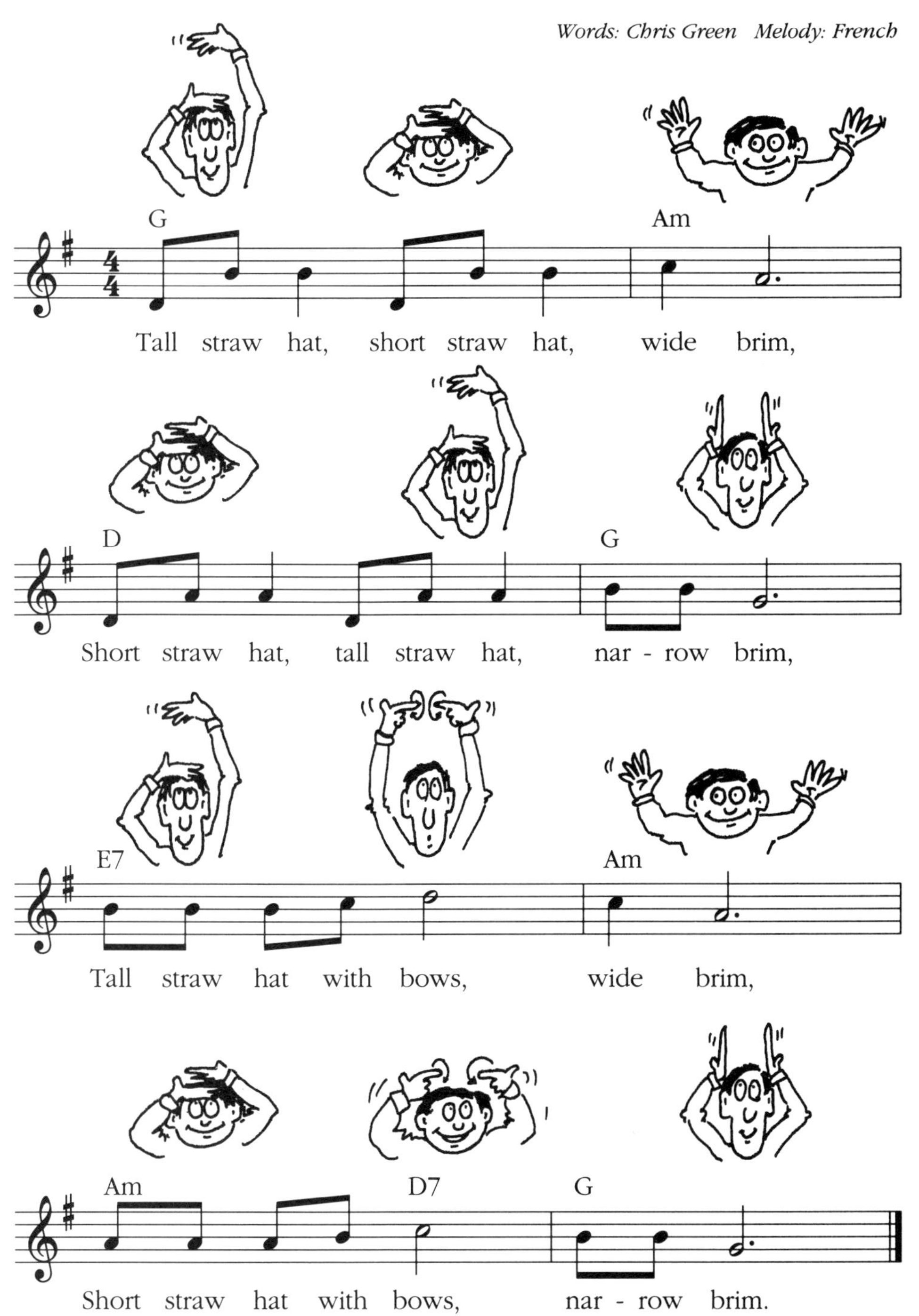

13 Nobody nose

Words and music: Kaye Umansky

Nobody knows where my nose has gone,
It was stuck on my face this morning,
A mischievous breeze combined with a sneeze,
And blew it away with no warning.
My nose blew off, my nose blew off,
My nose blew off with no warning.

Did anyone hear where my ears have gone?
They were here on my head this morning,
A terrible sound sent them spinning around
And they spun off my head with no warning.
My ears spun off, my ears spun off,
My nose blew off, my nose blew off,
My nose blew off with no warning.

Does anyone care where my hair has gone?
It was there on my head this morning,
I put on my hat and it didn't like that
So it fell off my head with no warning.
My hair fell off, my hair fell off,
My ears spun off, my ears spun off,
My nose blew off, my nose blew off,
My nose blew off with no warning.

That's odd! Do you know where my body has gone?
It was under my neck this morning,
I wanted to play but it wandered away,
Just walked out the door with no warning.
My body walked off, my body walked off,
My hair fell off, my hair fell off,
My ears spun off, my ears spun off,
My nose blew off, my nose blew off,
My nose blew off with no warning.

14 Frog song

Traditional, collected by Nancy Kerr

'Mm – mm!' said the little green frog one day,

'Mm – mm!' said the little green frog,

'Mm – mm!' said the little green frog one day,

And the frog went, 'Mm – mm – mm!'

But we know frogs go *clap*, 'La la la la la! *clap*

La la la la la! *clap* La la la la la!'

We know frogs go *clap* 'La la la la la.'

They don't go, 'Mm – mm – mm!'

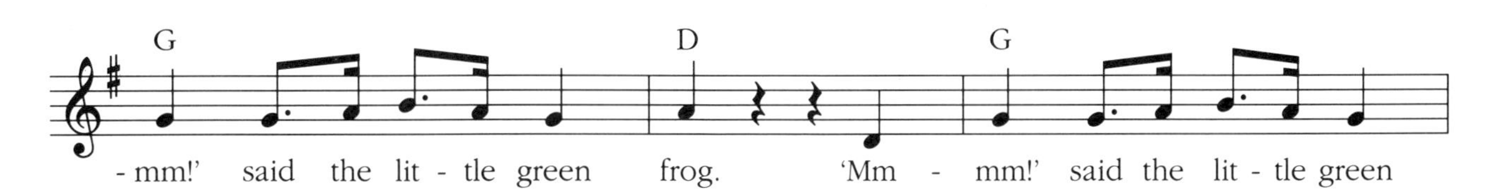

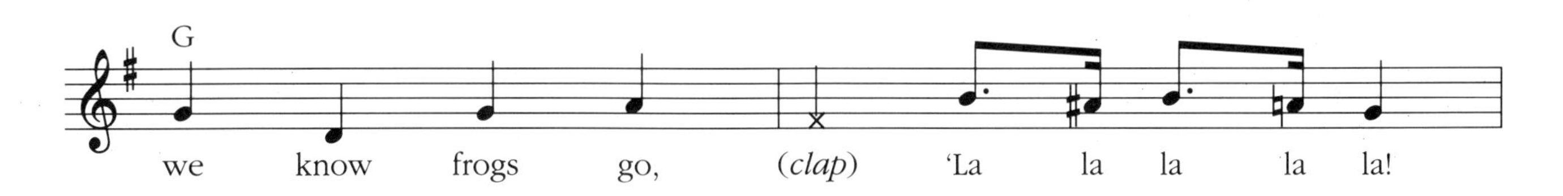

15 The biggest aspidistra in the world

Words and music: Jimmy Harper

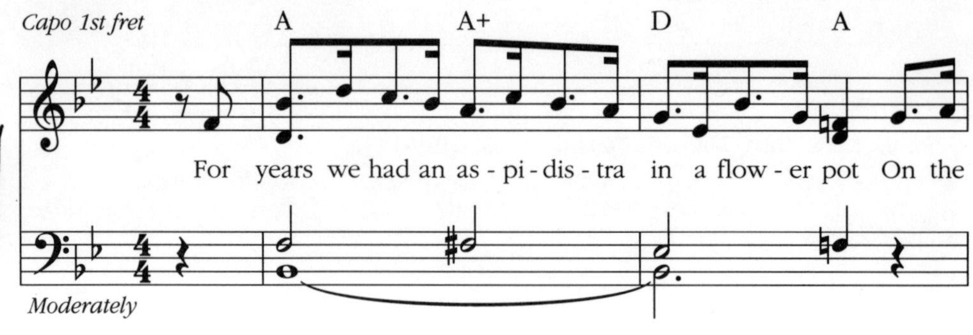

For years we had an aspidistra in a flower pot
On the what-not near the hat stand in the hall.
It didn't seem to grow, till one day our brother Joe
Had a notion that he'd make it strong and tall.
So he crossed it with an acorn from an oak tree
And he planted it against the garden wall.

It shot up like a rocket till it nearly touched the sky,
It's the biggest aspidistra in the world.
We couldn't see the top of it, it got so bloomin' high,
It's the biggest aspidistra in the world.
When father's had a skinful at his pub *The Bunch of Grapes*
He doesn't go all fighting mad and getting into scrapes -
You'll find him in his bear skin playing 'Tarzan of the Apes'
Up the biggest aspidistra in the world.

The tom cats and the moggies love to spend their evenings out
Up the biggest aspidistra in the world.
They all begin miaowing when the buds begin to sprout
From the biggest aspidistra in the world.
The dogs line up for miles and miles, a funny sight to see,
They sniff around for hours on end and wag their tails with glee,
So I've 'ad to put a notice up to say it's not a tree -
It's the biggest aspidistra in the world.

It's getting worn and weary and its leaves are turning grey,
It's the oldest aspidistra in the world.
So we water it with half a pint of Guinness every day,
It's the stoutest aspidistra in the world.
The Borough Council told us that we've got to chop it down,
It interferes with aeroplanes that fly above the town,
So we sold it to a wood yard for a lousy half a crown,
It's the biggest aspidistra in the world.

Em A7 D(sus) D A B Bm E7
crossed it with an a - corn from an oak tree, And he plant - ed it a - gainst the gar - den wall.
A E7 Bm
It shot up like a rock - et till it near - ly touched the sky, It's the big - gest as - pi - dis - tra in the world. We could - n't see the top of it, it
E7 A C♯m G♯ C♯m
got so bloom - in' high, It's the big - gest as - pi - dis - tra in the world. When fa - ther's had a skin - ful at his pub *The Bunch of Grapes,* He
Am B7 E7 A (A+) D Bm E7 Bm E7 A
does - n't go all fight - ing mad, and get - ting in - to scrapes – You'll find him in his bear - skin play - ing 'Tar - zan of the Apes' Up the big - gest as - pi - dis - tra in the world.

16 In Frisco Bay there lives a whale

Traditional North American

In Frisco Bay there lives a whale
And she eats peanuts by the pail,
And washtubs, and bathtubs, and sailboats,
and schooners.

Her name is Sara and she's a peach
But don't leave food within her reach,
Or babies, or nursemaids, or chocolate
ice cream sodas.

She loves to smile, and when she smiles
You can see her teeth for miles and miles,
And her tonsils, and her spare ribs,
and things too fierce to mention.

She knows no games, so when she plays
She rolls her eyes for days and days,
She vibrates and yodels and breaks
the Ten Commandments.

Now what you gonna do in a case like that?
There's nothing to do but sit on your hat,
Or your toothbrush, or your best friend,
or anything else that's useless.

17 The other day I met a bear

Traditional North American

The other day *echo*
I met a bear *echo*
Out in the woods away out there.
The other day *echo*
I met a bear *echo*
Out in the woods away out there.

He looked at me, *echo*
I looked at him, *echo*
He sized up me, I sized up him.
He looked at me, *echo*
I looked at him, *echo*
He sized up me, I sized up him.

He said to me, *echo*
'Why don't you run? *echo*
I see you don't have any gun.'
repeat

I said to him, *echo*
'That's a good idea.' *echo*
'Come on now, feet, get out of here.'
repeat

And so I ran *echo*
Away from there, *echo*
But right behind me came that bear.
repeat

And then I saw *echo*
Ahead of me *echo*
A great big tree, oh, glory be!
repeat

The lowest branch *echo*
Was ten feet up, *echo*
I'd have to jump and trust my luck.
repeat

And so I jumped *echo*
Into the air *echo*
But missed the branch away up
there.
repeat

But don't you fret *echo*
And don't you frown, *echo*
I caught that branch on the way
down.
repeat

That's all there is, *echo*
There ain't no more *echo*
Unless I see that bear once more.
repeat

Dramatise the story with actions.

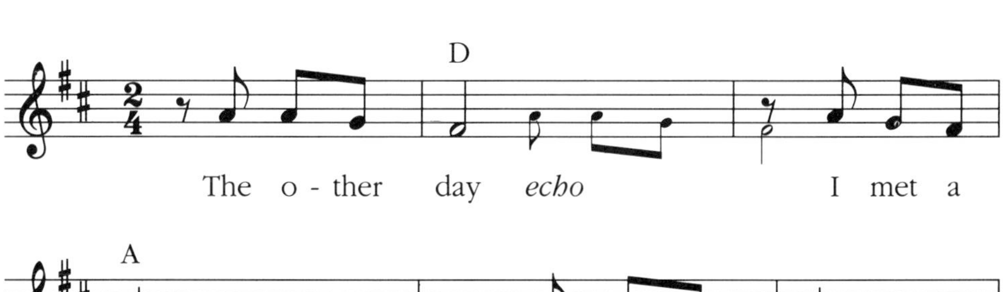

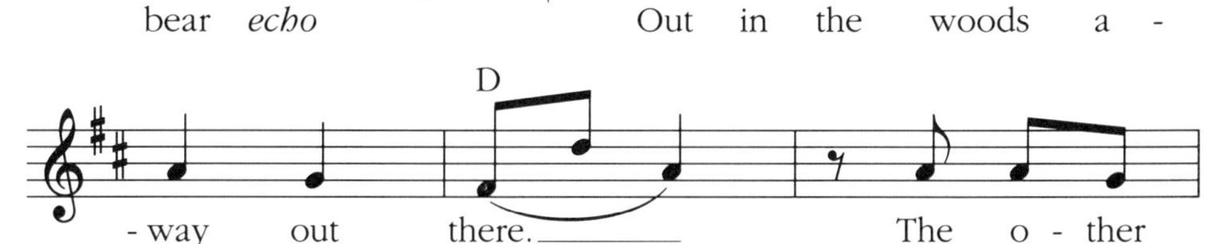

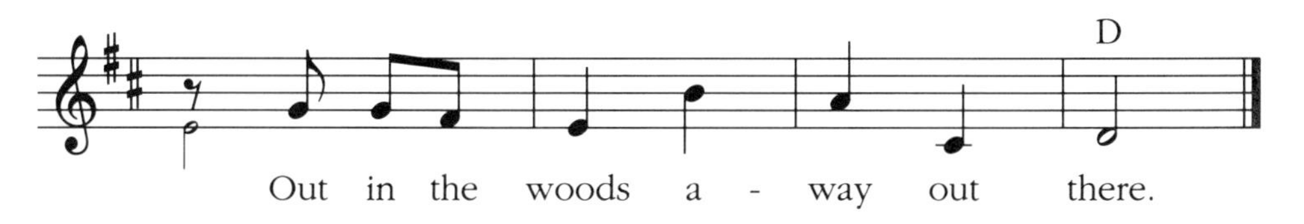

18 The Court of King Caractacus

Words and music: Rolf Harris

Now the ladies in the carriage
of the Court of King Caractacus
Were just passing by.
Now the ladies in the carriage
of the Court of King Caractacus
Were just passing by.
Now the ladies in the carriage
of the Court of King Caractacus
Were just passing by.
Now the ladies in the carriage
of the Court of King Caractacus
Were just passing by.

Now the noses on the faces
of the ladies in the carriage
of the Court of King Caractacus
Were just passing by ...

Now the boys who put the powder
on the noses on the faces
of the ladies in the carriage
of the Court of King Caractacus
Were just passing by ...

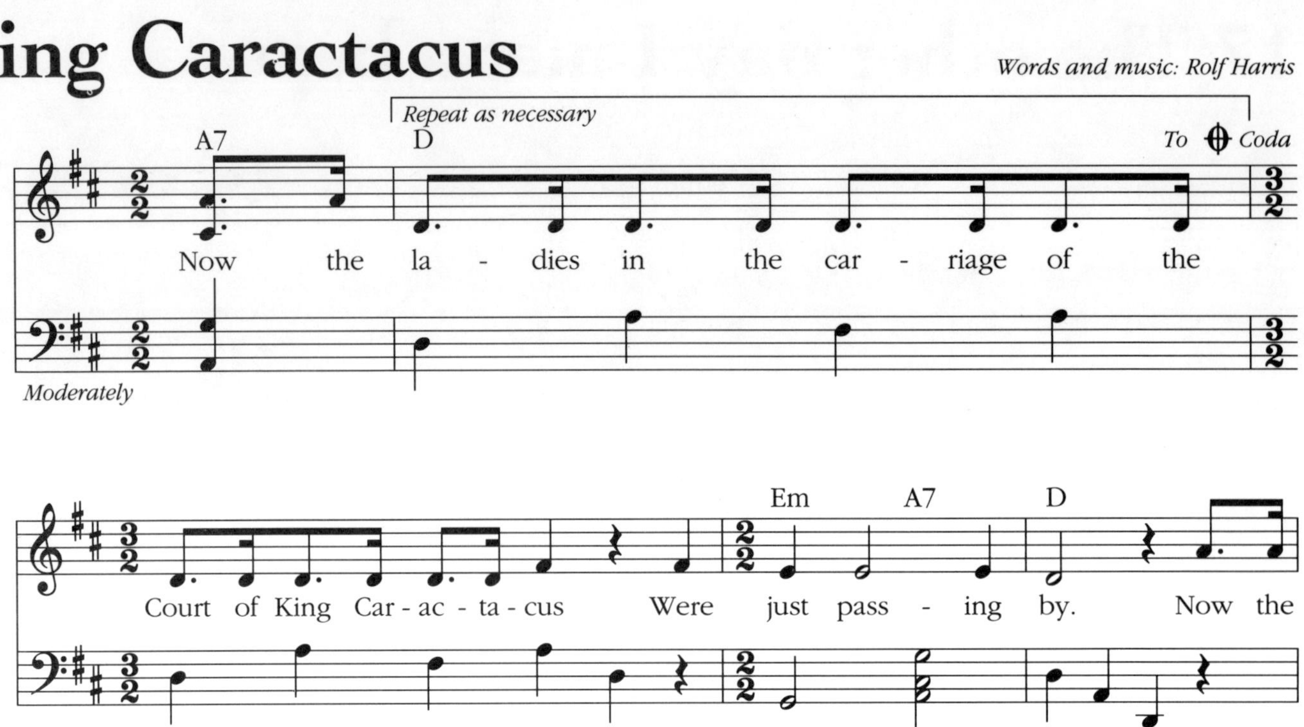

Now the fascinating witches who put
scintillating stitches in the britches
of the boys who put the powder
on the noses on the faces
of the ladies in the carriage
of the Court of King Caractacus
Were just passing by.

Now the fleas that gave the itches
to the fascinating witches who put
scintillating stitches in the britches
of the boys who put the powder
on the noses on the faces
of the ladies in the carriage
of the Court of King Caractacus
Were just passing by.

Now if you want to take some pictures
of the fleas that gave the itches
to the fascinating witches who put
scintillating stitches in the britches
of the boys who put the powder
on the noses on the faces
of the ladies in the carriage
of the Court of King Caractacus,
Spoken Well, you're too late!
Because they've just passed by.

19 My old banjo

I ululused to playlaylay my ololold banjololo
And relelest it ololon my kneeleeleeleeleeleelee,
But nowlowlow my strililings are brolololoken alaland
It's nololo more ululuse to melelelelelele.

I tooloolook it tololo the melelender's sholop
To seeleelee what helele could dolololololo,
He sailailaid your strililings are brolololoken alaland
It's nololo more ululuse to youlouloulouloulou.

Try 'I used to play my old bagpipes ...' to the tune of Auld Lang Syne. *Sing in* ***bagpiper*** *style.*

20 Apples and bananas

Traditional

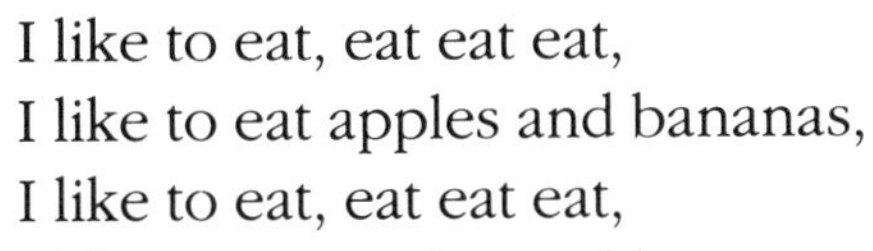

I like to eat, eat eat eat,
I like to eat apples and bananas,
I like to eat, eat eat eat,
I like to eat apples and bananas.

I like to ayt, ayt ayt ayt,
I like to ayt aypples and baynaynays,
I like to ayt, ayt ayt ayt,
I like to ayt aypples and baynaynays.

I like to eet, eet eet eet,
I like to eet eepples and beeneenees,
I like to eet, eet eet eet,
I like to eet eepples and beeneenees.

I like to ite, ite ite ite,
I like to ite iples and bininis,
I like to ite, ite ite ite,
I like to ite iples and bininis.

I like to ote, ote ote ote,
I like to ote oples and bononos,
I like to ote, ote ote ote,
I like to ote oples and bononos.

I like to oot, oot oot oot,
I like to oot ooples and boonoonoos,
I like to oot, oot oot oot,
I like to oot ooples and boonoonoos.

Now we're through, through through through,
Now we're through with the apples and bananas,
Now we're through, through through through,
With A E I O U.

21 Tiffy taffy

Tiffy taffy toffee
On the flee flo floor.
Tiffy taffy toffee
On the dee doe door.
Kiffy kaffy coffee
In a jig jag jug.
Kiffy kaffy coffee
In a mig mag mug.

Michael Rosen

22 No L

A B C D E F G
H I J K M N
O P Q R S T
U V W X Y Z
No L, no L, no L, no L,
No L, no L, no L, no L.

TUNE: *The First Noel*

23 Ging gang goolie

Traditional

Group A

Oompa oompa oompa ging gang
Goolie goolie goolie goolie woosha,
Ging gang goo, ging gang goo.
Ging gang goolie goolie goolie goolie woosha,
Ging gang goo, ging gang goo.
  Hayla, oh hayla shayla,
  Oh, hayla shayla hayla hoo-oo,
  Hayla, oh hayla shayla,
  Oh, hayla shayla hayla hoo.

Group B

Oompa oompa oompa oompa,
Oompa oompa oompa oompa,
Oompa oompa oompa oompa,
Oompa oompa oompa oompa,
Oompa oompa oomp.
  Oh, hayla shayla, oh hayla hayla shayla,
  Oh, hayla shayla, oh hayla shayla hoo.
  Oh, hayla shayla, oh hayla hayla shayla,
  Oh, hayla shayla, oh hayla shayla hoo.

24 Back slang

H - key
A - key
L - key
L - key
O - key jug

This is key jug *language. Say* key *after every letter in a word, and* key jug *after the last letter. Try to make it as fast and as rhythmic as possible.*

More back slangs:

1. *Take the last letter off the end of the word and put it on the front. So this last sentence would be -* Etak eth tlas rlette fof eth den fo eth dwor dan tpu ti no eth tfron.
2. *Put* arragay *on the end of every word.* Likearragay thisarragay.
3. *Say* errev *in the first syllable of each word then say the syllable -* Herrevappy berrevirthday terrevo yerrevou!
4. *Bacon-slices - break the word up letter by letter -*

everybody
verybody
erybody
rybody (pronounced *rye-body*)
ybody (pronounced *why-body*)
body
ody
dy (pronounced *die*)
y (pronounced *why*)

Say it very fast. Try doing the same with calamity, catastrophe, shampoo ...

Group A

Oompa oompa oompa, kwik kwak
Kwannie kwannie kwannie kwannie nash nick,
Kwik kwak kwee, kwik kwak kwo,
Kwik kwak kwannie kwannie kwannie
kwannie nash nick,
Kwick kwak kwee, kwik kwak kwo.
Kwannie, oh kwannie kwannie,
Oh, kwannie kwannie kwannie amo,
Kwannie, oh kwannie kwannie,
Oh, kwannie kwannie kwannie kwo.

Group B

Oompa oompa oompa oompa …
Oh nicodema, oh kwannie kwannie amo,
Oh nicodema, oh kwannie kwannie kwo,
Oh nicodema, oh kwannie kwannie amo,
Oh nicodema, oh kwannie kwannie kwo.

Group A

Oompa oompa oompa, kwee kwa
Kwuddy muddy muddy muddy dashnik,
Oompa kwee, oompa kwo,
Kwee kwa kwuddy muddy muddy muddy
dashnik,
Oompa kwee, oompa kwo.
Golly, oh golly olly,
Oh, golly olly golly amo,
Golly, oh golly olly,
Oh, golly olly olly mo.

Group B

Oompa oompa oompa oompa ...
Oh nicodemo, oh golly olly amo,
Oh nicodemo, oh golly olly mo,
Oh nicodemo, oh golly olly a mo,
Oh nicodemo, oh golly olly mo,

25 Jibber jabber

Words adapted from traditional by Michael Rosen *Music by Peter Gosling*

Jibber jabber, gabble, babble,
Cackle, clack and prate,
Twiddle, twaddle, mutter, stutter,
Utter, splutter, blate,
Chatter, patter, tattle, prattle,
Chew the rag and crack,
Spiel and spout and spit it out,
Tell the world and quack.
Jibber, jibber jabber,
Jibber jabber, jibber jabber,
You hoo hoo hoo.
Jibber, jibber jabber,
Jibber jabber, jibber jabber,
YOU!

Sniffle, snuffle, drawl and bawl,
Snicker, snort and snap,
Bark and buzz and yap and yelp,
Chin and chirp and chat,
Shout and shoot and gargle, gasp,
Gab and gag and groan,
Hem and haw and work the jaw,
Grumble, mumble, moan.
Jibber, jibber jabber ...

Natter, blather, yack and gas,
Waffle on and wail,
State your case and spin a yarn,
Rant and rave and rail,
Beef and bellyache and bat,
Say a mouthful, squawk,
That is what some people do
When they merely talk.
Jibber, jibber jabber ...

26 Back chat

 Are you the guy

 That told the guy

 That I'm the guy

 Who gave the guy

 The black eye?

 No, I'm not the guy

 Who told the guy

 That you're the guy

 Who gave the guy

 The black eye.

You remind me of a man
What man?
A man of power.
What power?
The power of hoodoo
Who do?
You do
Do what?
Remind me of a man.
What man?

continue getting faster and faster

See you later, alligator
In a while, crocodile
See you later, hot potato
If you wish, jelly-fish
Not too soon, you big baboon
Toodle-oo, kangaroo
Bye-bye, butter fly
See you tomorrow, horror
In a week, freak ...

continue adding your own

Says she to me
Is that you?
Says I, who?
Says she, you!
Says I, me?
Says she, aye.
Says I, no.
Says she, oh!
It's awfee like you.

Aim to do all these at speed. Split into two groups - one for the question, one for the answer.

27 I'm a little wrong note

Words and music: Arthur Askey

I'm a little wrong note, running round the band,
Getting into mischief, isn't it grand.
Oozing through the oboe, booming on the bass,
Everybody after me - oh! what a chase.
Popping in the piccolo, dancing on the drum,
I'm a little wrong note - here I come.

I'm a little wrong note, running round the band,
Getting into mischief, isn't it grand.
Nobody can catch me when I'm on the run,
Tinkle tinkle crash crash - oh! what fun.
No-one likes to see me round the place because
I'm a little wrong note, here I was.

I'm a little wrong note, running round the band,
Getting into mischief, isn't it grand.
I'm a little nuisance, I'm a little imp,
Making the conductors go quite limp.
Then I bash the cymbal, strum on the guitar,
I'm a little wrong note - here I are.

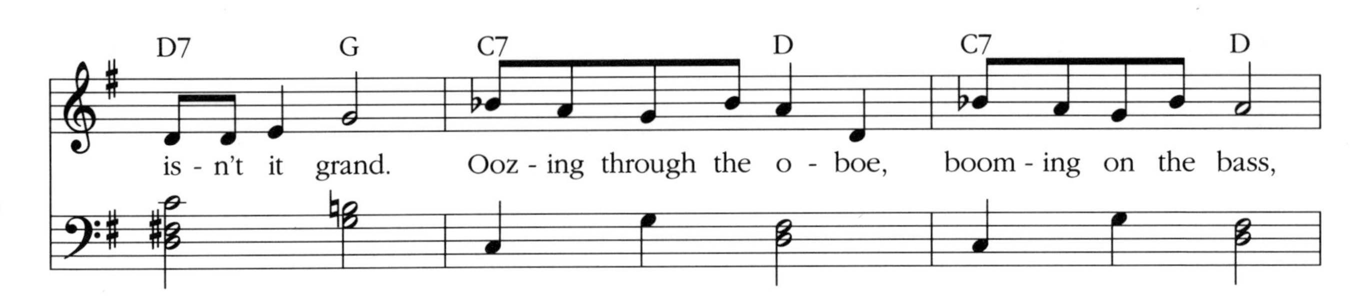

I'm a little wrong note, running round the band,
Getting into mischief, isn't it grand.
Now that I have told you all you want to know,
You wonder why they call me a little so-and-so.
Oompah oompah oompah - whizz whizz whizz,
I think I've found the right note - here it is.

Now we've found the right note -
hang on to it tight.
Cheerio playmates, night, night, night!

1. (Slightly slower)
F7 B♭ G7 C E♭7 D G G C
danc - ing on the drum, I'm a lit - tle wrong note, here I come!
G/D NC
2. (With mock solemnity)
G Am G C D NC
3. (Slowly)
G
G C♯° NC
4.
NC D7 G
G7 C7 F7 B♭7 E♭7 G/D D7 G
Now we've found the right note – hang on to it tight. Cheer - io play - mates, 'night, 'night, 'night!
* Insert any sound from the Silly Sounds page

28 Nel and Ned

Words and music: Morag Blance

Big Nell and Ned, *echo*
The elephant pair, *echo*
Started to climb *echo*
Noah's wooden stair. *echo*
Stepped on the back, *echo*
Why I do declare, *echo*
The front of the ark *echo*
Shot up in the air. *echo*
  Poor old Nell and Ned. Boo hoo hoo!
  Far too heavy for Noah's Ark,
  What will old Noah do?

They both came up *echo*
For a second time, *echo*
On the left hand side *echo*
Decided to climb. *echo*
Left side went low, *echo*
Right side went high, *echo*
Shot all the animals, *echo*
Into the sky. *echo*
  Poor old Nell and Ned. Boo hoo hoo ...

Then Mrs Noah *echo*
Said, 'Please pay heed, *echo*
An equal balance *echo*
Is all you need. *echo*
Put Nell one end, *echo*
Balance Ned on the other, *echo*
Then the Ark will float *echo*
In the flood no bother.' *echo*
  Lucky old Nell and Ned. This is true!
  Mrs Noah was good at maths -
  Knew exactly what to do!

***Silly sounds**: slurp water from end to end of a plastic bottle during the chorus.*

29 Bugs go wild, simply wild, over me

Traditional

Bugs go wild, simply wild, over me,
I'm referring to the bedbugs and the fleas.
Every morning, noon, and night all the
bugs how they do bite,
Bugs go wild, simply wild, over me.

In the morning on my pillowcase
A daddy-long-legs stares me in the face,
In my underpants and shoes they
assemble for a snooze,
Bugs go wild, simply wild, over me.

When I sit down to rest on a hike,
There are ants running left, running right,
There are spiders in my hair and
mosquitoes everywhere,
Bugs go wild, simply wild, over me.

***Silly sounds:** accompany with **bodyscratchers** in the places marked* *

30 The flies crawl up the window

Words: Douglas Furber Music: Vivian Ellis

The flies crawl up the window
In sunshine and in rain;
They do not seek for pleasure,
They much prefer the pane.
And if those flies annoy you
Then here's what I advise -
Just don't have any windows
And then you will have no flies.
The flies crawl up the window,
It's all they have to do.
They go up by the thousand
And come down two by two.
The flies crawl up the window,
They say, 'We love to roam:
So once more up the window
And then we'll all go home.'

The flies crawled up the window
Then thought that they'd descend;
They all crawled for a fortnight
But didn't reach the end.
One breathless fly said, 'Blimey,
This is some window, Bill!'
It was the Crystal Palace,
So p'raps they're crawling still.
The flies crawled up the window ...

D7 G G7 Chorus C
you will have no flies. The flies crawl up the win - dow, It's
G G7
all they have to do. They go up by the thou - sand And come down two by
C G7 C
two. The flies crawl up the win - dow, They say, 'We love to
G G7 C
roam: So once more up the win - dow And then we'll all go home.'
The flies crawl up the window
And yet the fact remains,
You'll often meet with people
Who say flies have no brains.
Next time you see flies crawling
Upside down upon a shelf,
If you don't think that's clever
Just try it for yourself.

31 Susanna's a funniful cow

Traditional

There was an old farmer, he had an old sow,
-ow, -ow, -idle-ee-dow,
Susanna's a funniful man,
-an, -an, -idle-ee-dan,
Susanna's a funniful man.
Sing lasses go ring ra la,
Susanna's a funniful cow,
-ow, -ow, -idle-ee-dow,
Susanna's a funniful cow.

Now this old sow she had some pigs,
-igs, -igs, -idle-ee-digs,
Susanna's a funniful man,
-an, -an, -idle-ee-dan,
Susanna's a funniful man.
Sing lasses go ring ra la ...

Now these little pigs they had curly tails,
-ails, -ails, -idle-ee-dails,
Susanna's a funniful man,
-an, -an, -idle-ee-dan,
Susanna's a funniful man.
Sing lasses go ring ra la ...

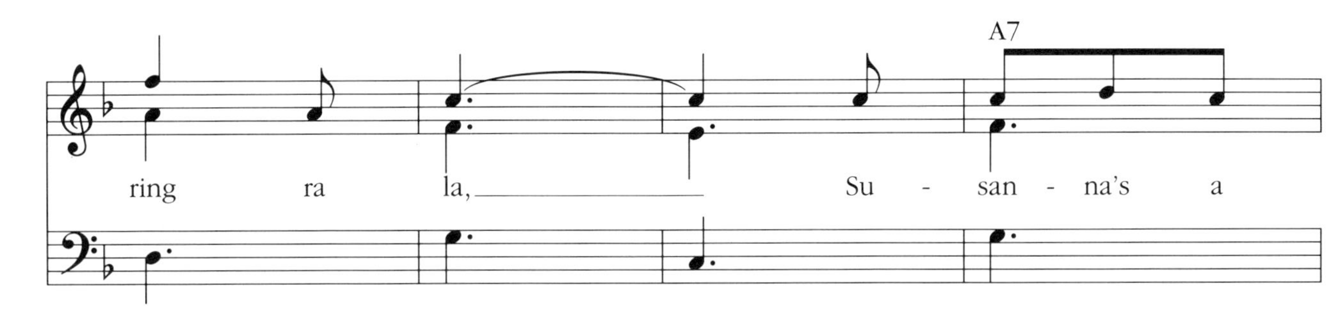

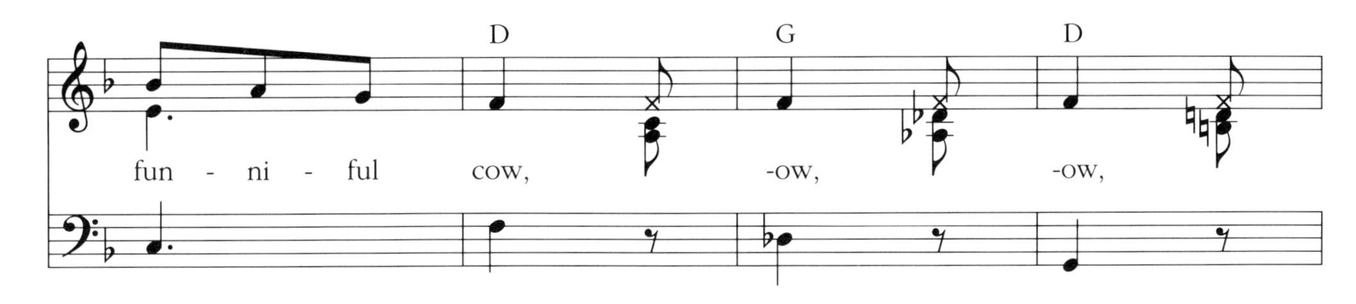

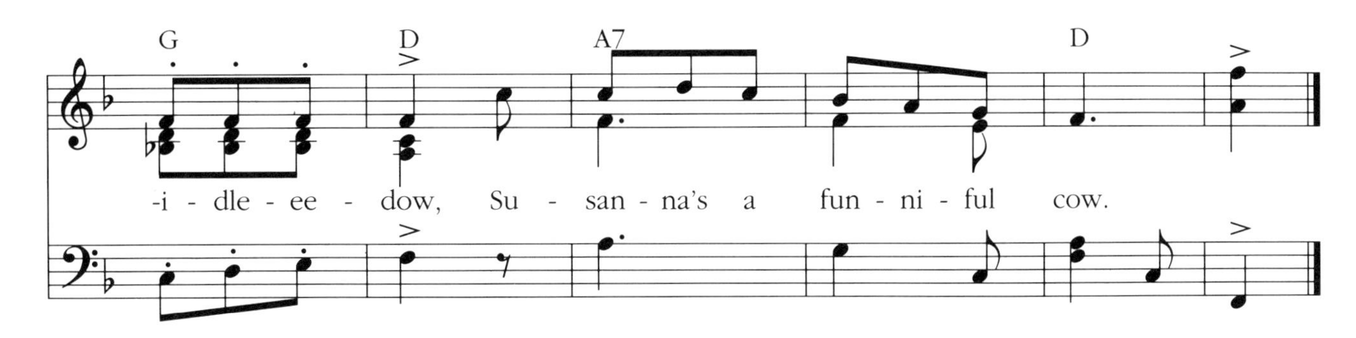

Now these little pigs they muddled them up,
up, up, idle-ee-dup,
Susanna's a funniful man,
-an, -an, -idle-ee-dan,
Susanna's a funniful man.
Sing lasses go ring ra la ...

Now these little pigs they made the best bacon,
-acon, -acon, -idle-ee-dacon,
Susanna's a funniful man,
-an, -an, -idle-ee-dan,
Susanna's a funniful man.
Sing lasses go ring ra la ...

Sadly and slowly

Now these little pigs they grunted no more, *(pause)*
(go like the clappers)
-ore, -ore, -idle-ee-dore,
Susanna's a funniful man,
-an, -an, -idle-ee-dan,
Susanna's a funniful man.

At snort, at blow a raspberry, at whistle

32 High hopes

Next time you're found with your chin
on the ground,
There's a lot to be learned, so look around.
Just what makes that little old ant
Think he'll move that rubber tree plant?
Anyone knows an ant can't move a rubber tree plant.
But he's got high hopes, he's got high hopes;
He's got high apple pie in the sky hopes.
So any time you're gettin' low,
'Stead of lettin' go, just remember that ant.
Oops! There goes another rubber tree plant. *echo*
Oops! There goes another rubber tree plant.

When troubles call and your back's to the wall,
There's a lot to be learned, that wall could fall.
Once there was a silly old ram,
Thought he'd punch a hole in a dam;
No one could make that ram scram, he kept
buttin' that dam.
'Cause he had high hopes, he had high hopes;
He had high apple pie in the sky hopes.
So any time you're feelin' bad,
'Stead of feelin' sad, just remember that ram.
Oops! There goes a billion kilowatt dam. *echo*
Oops! There goes a billion kilowatt dam.

So keep your high hopes, keep your high hopes;
Keep those high apple pie in the sky hopes.
A problem's just a toy balloon,
They'll be bursting soon,
They're just bound to go 'Pop!'
Oops! There goes another problem, kerplop! *echo*
Oops! There goes another problem, kerplop!
Kerplop!

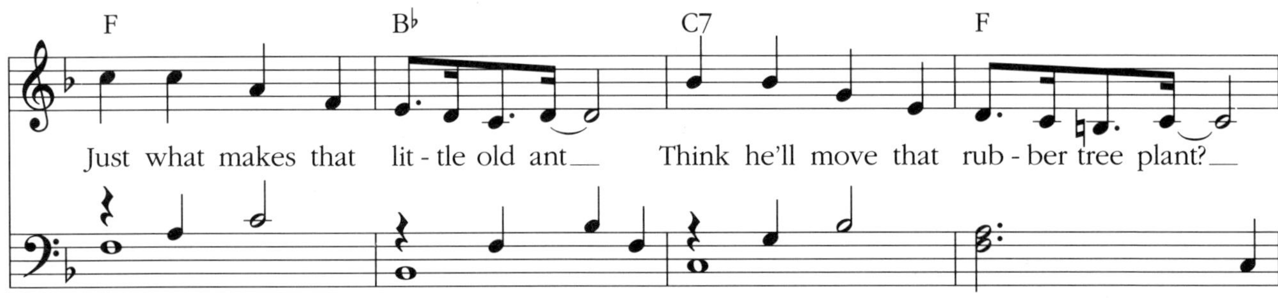

B♭ (B°) F Dm7 G7
high hopes, he's got high hopes; He's got high ap - ple pie in the
C7 F F7 B♭ (B°)
sky hopes. So an - y time you're get - ting low, 'Stead of let - ting go, just re - mem - ber that ant.
Gm (F♯°) Gm C7 F Dm Gm C7 F Dm
Oops! there goes an - oth - er rub - ber tree plant! Oops! there goes an -
(Oops! There goes an - oth - er rub - ber tree plant!)
1. 2. 3.
Gm C7 F (F♯°) Gm C7 F C7 F7 D.S. F C7 F
- oth - er rub - ber tree plant! dam. So keep your plop! Ker - plop!
3

33 A G-nu

Words: Michael Flanders Music: Michael Flanders and Donald Swann

I'm a G-nu, I'm a G-nu,
The g-nicest work of g-nature in the zoo!
I'm a G-nu, how do you do?
You really ought to k-now w-ho's w-ho.
I'm a G-nu, spelt G. N. U.
I'm g-not a camel or a kangaroo,
So let me introduce,
I'm g-neither man or moose,
Oh, g-no, g-no, g-no,
I'm a G-nu!

I'm a G-nu, ag-nother G-nu,
I wish I could g-nash my teeth at you,
I'm a G-nu, how do you do?
You really ought to k-now w-ho's w-ho.
I'm a G-nu, spelt G.N.U.
Call me bison or okapi and I'll sue,
G-nor am I in the least
Like that dreadful hartebeest
Oh, g-no, g-no, g-no,
I'm a G-nu!

D A D
-ho. I'm a G - nu, Spelt G. N.
Am D7
U. I'm g - not a ca - mel or a kan - ga -
G Em E
-roo, So let me in - tro - duce, I'm g -
D B7 E A7 D A7 D
-nei - ther Man or Moose, Oh g - no, g - no, g - no, I'm a G - nu!

G-NOSE WAVE
① Cross hands (left hand on top).
② Place palms together and interlace fingers.
③ Bend hands down and round and in towards you.
④ Put nose between back of index fingers.......
⑤ Undo hands and waggle fingers while still holding nose between index fingers!
HAVE A G'NICE DAY!

34 Hobble gobble wobble

Michael Rosen

It was a stormy night on a Christmas day,
As they fell awake on the Santa Fe.

The ship in the dock was at the end of its trip,
And the man on board was the captain of the ship.

The name of the man was old Ben Brown
And he played the ukelele with his trousers down.

Turkey, jelly and the ship's old cook
All jumped out of a recipe book.

The jelly wobbled, the turkey gobbled
And after them both the old cook hobbled.

Gobbler gobbled Hobbler's Wobbler,
Hobbler gobbled Wobbler's Gobbler.

Gobbly-gobbler gobbled Wobbly,
Hobbly-hobbler gobbled Gobbly.

Gobble gobbled Hobble's Wobble,
Hobble gobbled gobbled Wobble.

Gobble gobble wobble wobble
Hobble gobble wobble gobble.

35 Busy day

Michael Rosen

Pop in pop out, pop over the road,
Pop out for a walk, pop in for a talk,
Pop down to the shop, can't stop! — pop pop
Got to pop! — pop pop, got to pop? — pop pop,
Pop where? — pop pop, pop what? — pop pop.

Pop round pop up, pop into town,
Pop out and see, pop in for tea,
Pop down to the shop, can't stop! — pop pop,
Got to pop! — pop pop, got to pop? — pop pop,
Pop where? — pop pop, pop what? — pop pop.

Say this with a steady beat like a rap. Use ***beatbox*** *as a continuous background sound, and* ***poppers*** *at* pop pop. *End with a random burst of* ***poppers***.

36 A trip to Morrow

Words: anon Melody: adapted by SR

I started on a journey just about a week ago
For the little town of Morrow in the State of Ohio.
I never was a traveller and I really didn't know
That Morrow had been ridiculed a century or so.
To Morrow, to Morrow, I have to go to Morrow,
The ticket collector told me that I have to go tomorrow.

I went down to the depot for my ticket and applied
For tips regarding Morrow, interviewed the station guide.
Said I, 'My friend, I want to go to Morrow and return
No later than tomorrow, for I haven't time to burn.'
To Morrow, to Morrow, I have to go to Morrow,
The ticket collector told me that I have to go tomorrow.

Said he to me, 'Now let me see, if I have heard you right,
You want to go to Morrow and come back tomorrow night,
You should have gone to Morrow yesterday and back today,
The train to Morrow, left at two to Morrow yesterday.
To Morrow, to Morrow, I have to go to Morrow,
The ticket collector told me that I have to go tomorrow.

For if you started yesterday to Morrow, don't you see
You should have got to Morrow and returned today at three.
The train that started yesterday, now understand me right,
Today it gets to Morrow and returns tomorrow night.'
To Morrow, to Morrow, I have to go to Morrow,
The ticket collector told me that I have to go tomorrow.

Said I, 'I guess you know it all, but kindly let me say,
How can I go to Morrow if I leave the town today?'
Said he, 'You cannot go to Morrow today I'll have you know,
For that train you see just leaving is the only one to go. So –
Tomorrow, tomorrow, you'll have to go tomorrow,
The train to Morrow just left today, you'll have to go tomorrow.

37 A poor old man was crossing the road

Adapted from traditional by The Singing Kettle

A poor old man was crossing the road,
Crossing the road, crossing the road,
A poor old man was crossing the road,
When along came a wheelbarrow.
Don't let the wheel of your wheelbarrow,
Your wheelbarrow, your wheelbarrow,
Don't let the wheel of your wheelbarrow,
Run over the poor old man.

A poor old man was crossing the road ...
When along came a fish and chip potato van,
wheelbarrow.
Don't let the wheels of your fish and chip
potato van, wheelbarrow,
Your fish and chip potato van, wheelbarrow,
your fish and chip potato van,
wheelbarrow,
Don't let the wheels of your fish and chip
potato van, wheelbarrow,
Run over the poor old man.

A poor old man was crossing the road ...
When along came a trolley bus with no wipers,
fish and chip potato van, wheelbarrow.
Don't let the wheels of your trolley bus with
no wipers, fish and chip potato van,
wheelbarrow ...
Run over the poor old man.

38 Wizz Kings

Adapt as necessary

Em A7 D

wheel - bar - row Run o - ver the poor old man.

Try to keep the beat going as you fit in more and more vehicles. For example bars 8-10 of the second verse go:

We three kings of Orient are,
One in a taxi,
One in a car,
One in a scooter,
Blowing his hooter,
Smoking a big cigar.

TUNE: *We three kings*

A poor old man was crossing the road ...
When along came a Glasgow Corporation cart
which sucks water out of drains, trolley bus
with no wipers, fish and chip potato van,
wheelbarrow.
Don't let the wheels of your Glasgow Corporation
cart which sucks water out of drains, trolley
bus with no wipers, fish and chip potato van,
wheelbarrow ...
Run over the poor old man.

Change the vehicles if you like, and go on adding to them.

39 Star trekkin'

Star trekkin' across the universe
On the Starship Enterprise under Captain Kirk.
Star trekkin' across the universe,
Only going forward 'cause we can't find reverse.

There's Klingons on the starboard bow,
starboard bow, starboard bow.
There's Klingons on the starboard bow,
starboard bow, Jim.
Star trekkin' across the universe ...

Spock, spoken

It's life, Jim, but not as we know it,
not as we know it, not as we know it.
It's life, Jim, but not as we know it,
not as we know it, Capt'n.
There's Klingons on the starboard bow,
starboard bow, starboard bow.
There's Klingons on the starboard bow,
starboard bow, Jim.
Star trekkin' across the universe ...

Bones, spoken

It's worse than that, he's dead, Jim,
dead, Jim, dead, Jim,
It's worse than that, he's dead, Jim,
dead, Jim, dead.
It's life, Jim, but not as we know it ...
There's Klingons on the starboard bow ...
Star trekkin' across the universe ...

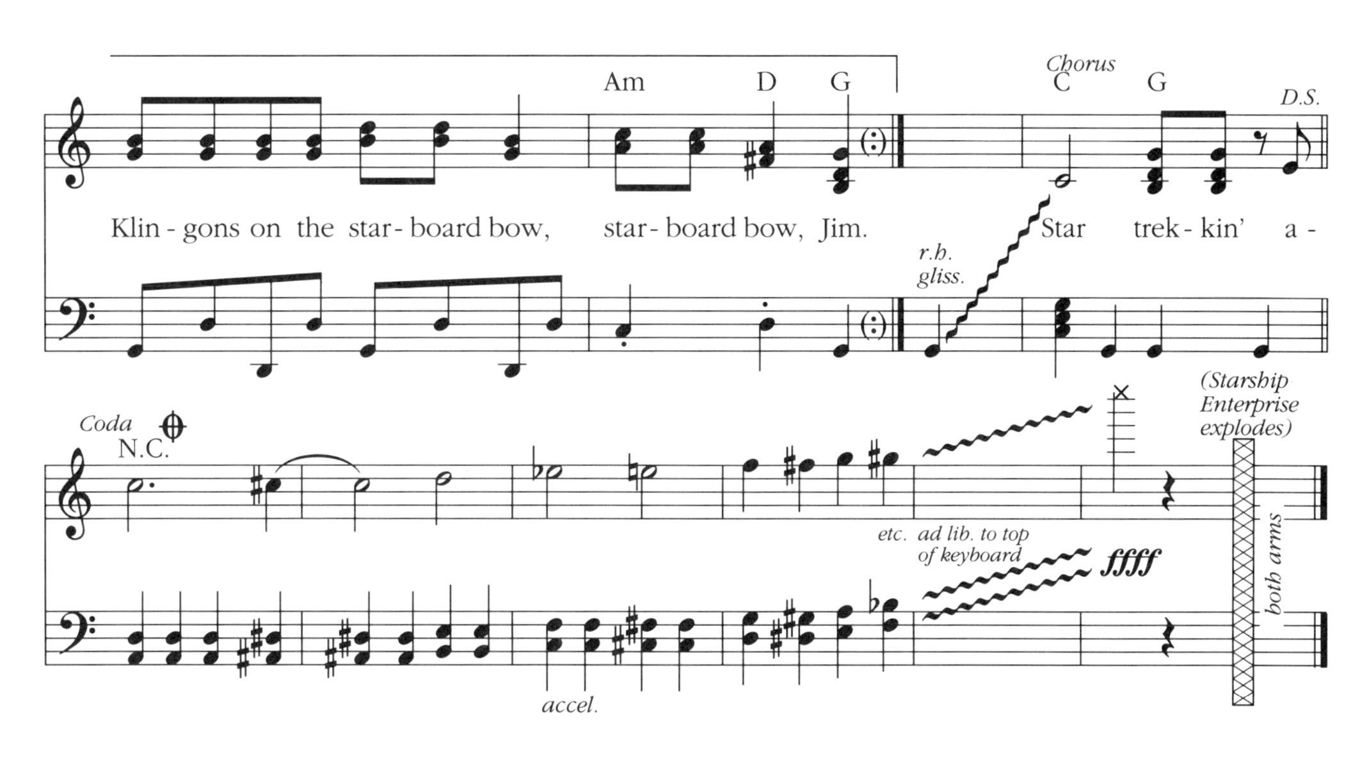

Kirk, spoken

We come in peace, shoot to kill,
shoot to kill, shoot to kill,
We come in peace, shoot to kill,
shoot to kill, SHOOT!
It's worse than that, he's dead, Jim ...
It's life, Jim, but not as we know it ...
There's Klingons on the starboard bow ...
Star trekkin' across the universe ...

Scottie, spoken

Ye canny change the laws of physics,
laws of physics, laws of physics,
Ye canny change the laws of physics,
ye canny change the laws.
We come in peace, shoot to kill ...
It's worse than that, he's dead, Jim ...
It's life, Jim, but not as we know it ...
There's Klingons on the starboard bow ...
Scrape 'em off, Jim.
Star trekkin' across the universe ...

Silly sounds: *use* ***aeroplane*** *for a continuous background noise.*

40 Down in the valley where nobody goes

Down in the valley where nobody goes,
There's a great big crocodile washing his clothes,
With a scrubba scrub here, and a scrubba scrub there,
That's the way he washes his clothes.
With an i tie oogie boogie woogie,
With an i tie oogie boogie woogie,
With an i tie oogie boogie woogie,
That's the way he washes his clothes.

Down in the valley where nobody goes,
There's a great big bumble bee washing her clothes,
With a buzzy-wuzz here, and a buzzy-wuzz there,
That's the way she washes her clothes.
With an i tie oogie boogie woogie ...

Add on as many different animals and actions and silly sounds as you like. Here are some suggestions:

elephant *- wave trunk*
snake *- arm makes snaky movements*
tiger *- bare teeth and show claws*
alien/monster/goon *- do the whole verse and chorus in a wobbly blobby way.*

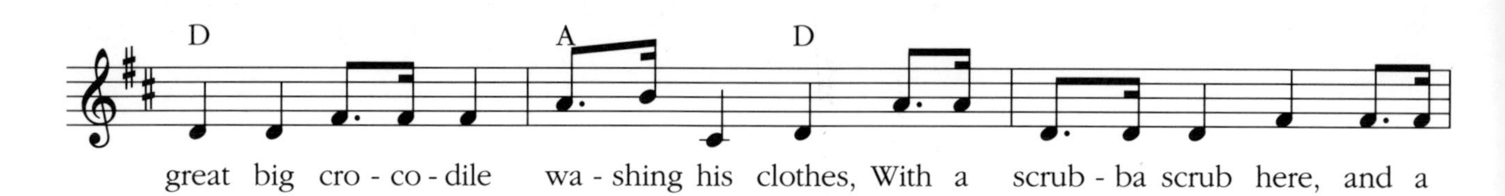

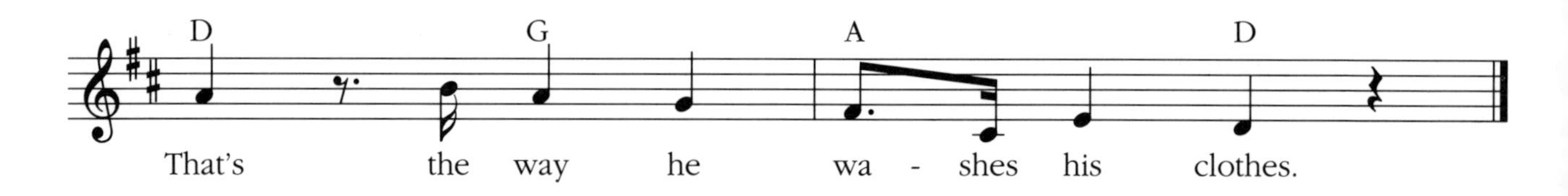

41 Shark song

Traditional, collected by Nancy Kerr

Doo-doo, doo bedee doo,
Doo-doo, doo bedee doo.

There was a boy,
Doo-doo, doo bedee doo.
There was a girl,
Doo-doo, doo bedee doo.
They went for a swim,
Doo-doo, doo bedee doo.
A swim in the sea.
Doo-doo, doo bedee doo.
They took off their clothes,
Doo-doo, doo bedee doo.
All of their clothes,
Doo-doo, doo bedee doo.
They swam so far,
Doo-doo, doo bedee doo.
Really far,
Doo-doo, doo bedee doo.
There was no one around,
Doo-doo, doo bedee doo.
Just no one around,
very quietly
Doo-doo, doo bedee doo.
Totally empty,
Doo-doo, doo bedee doo.
Completely unpopulated,
Doo-doo, doo bedee doo.
Except for the SHARKS!

all make shape of sharks' jaws with arms
Na-na, na na na na!
Daddy shark,
Na-na, na na na na!
Mummy shark,
Na-na, na na na na!
mime gummy shark
Granpa shark,
Ma-ma, ma ma ma ma!
mime little shark's mouth
Baby shark,
Wee wee, wee wee wee wee!
They swam so fast,
get faster
Doo-doo, doo bedee doo,
Really fast,
Doo-doo, doo bedee doo,
To the shore,
Doo-doo, doo bedee doo,
Out of the water,
Doo-doo, doo bedee doo,
Ran so fast,
Doo-doo, doo bedee doo,
Really fast,
Doo-doo, doo bedee doo,

There was no one around,
slow down again
Doo-doo, doo bedee doo,
Totally empty,
Doo-doo, doo bedee doo,
Devoid of habitation,
whisper
Doo-doo, doo bedee doo,
EXCEPT FOR THE SHARKS!

The repeated lines doo-doo *and* na-na *can be sung by a group keeping the beat with* ***fingerclicks***. *The other lines can be sung by a soloist or second group.*

42 Purple People Eater

Well, I saw the thing a-comin' out of the sky,
It had one long horn and one big eye.
I commenced to shakin' and I said, 'Ooh-wee,
It looks like a Purple People Eater to me.'

First chorus

It was a one-eyed, one-horned, flyin' Purple People Eater,
One-eyed, one-horned, flyin' Purple People Eater,
One-eyed, one-horned, flyin' Purple People Eater,
Sure looked strange to me.

Well, he came down to earth and he lit in a tree,
I said, 'Mister Purple People Eater, don't eat me.'
I heard him say in a voice so gruff,
'I wouldn't eat you 'cause you're so tough.'

Second chorus

Well bless my soul, rock'n roll, flyin' Purple People Eater,
Pidgeon-toed, under-growed, flyin' Purple People Eater,
He wears short shorts, friendly little People Eater,
What a sight to see.

I said, 'Mister Purple People Eater, what's your line?'
He said, 'Eatin' purple people, and it sure is fine,
But that's not the reason that I came to land,
I wanna get a job in a rock and roll band.'

First chorus

Words and music: Sheb Wooley

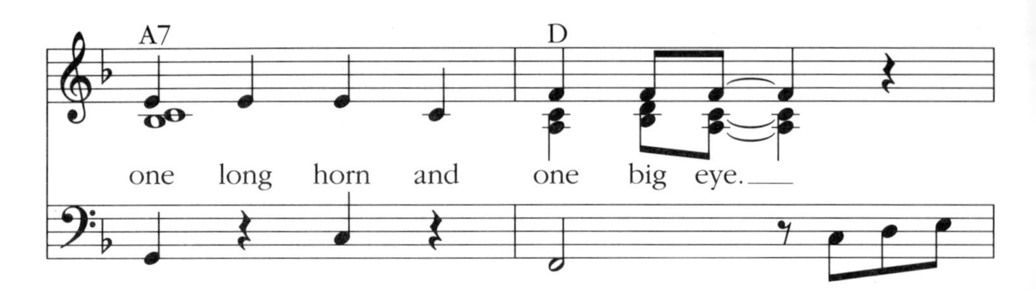

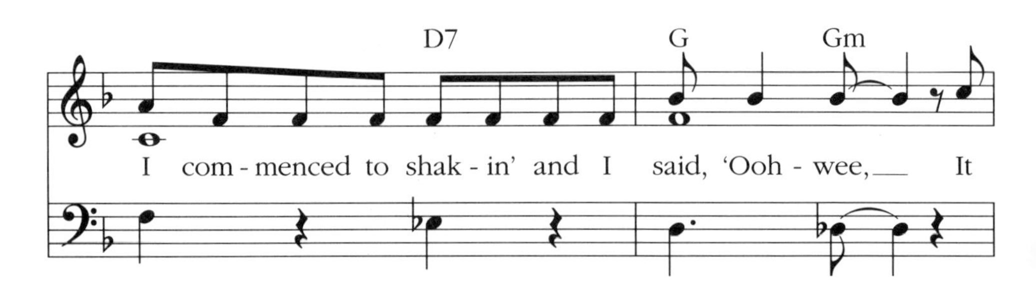

And then he swung from the tree and he lit on the ground,
And he started to rock, a-really rockin' around.
It was a crazy ditty with a swingin' tune,
Singa bop bapa loop a lap a loom bam boom.

Second chorus

Well he went on his way and then what-a you know,
I saw him last night on a tv show.
He was blowin' it out, really knockin' 'em dead.
Rock'n roll music going round in his head.

First chorus

43 The Thing

Words and music: Charles R. Grean

While I was walking down the beach one bright and sunny day,
I saw a great big wooden box a-floatin' in the bay.
I pulled it in and opened it up and much to my surprise,
Oh, I discovered a *stamp stamp* right before my eyes,
Oh, I discovered a *stamp stamp* right before my eyes.

I picked it up and ran to town as happy as a king,
I took it to a guy I know who'd buy most anything
But this is what he hollered at me as I walked in his shop:
Oh, get out of here with that *stamp stamp* before I call a cop …

I turned around and got right out, a-runnin' for my life,
And then I took it home with me to give it to my wife,
But this is what she hollered at me as I walked in the door:
Oh, get out of here with that *stamp stamp* and don't come back no more …

I wandered all around the town until I chanced to meet
A hobo who was looking for a handout on the street.
He said he'd take most any old thing, he was a desperate man,
But when I showed him the *stamp stamp* he turned around and ran …

I wandered on for many years, a victim of my fate,
Until one day I came upon Saint Peter at the gate,
And when I tried to take it inside he told me where to go:
Get out of here with that *stamp stamp* and take it down below …

The moral of the story is if you're out on the beach
And you should see a great big box and it's within your reach,
Don't ever stop and open it up, that's my advice to you,
'Cause you'll never get rid of the *stamp stamp* no matter what you do,
Oh, you'll never get rid of the *stamp stamp* no matter what you do.

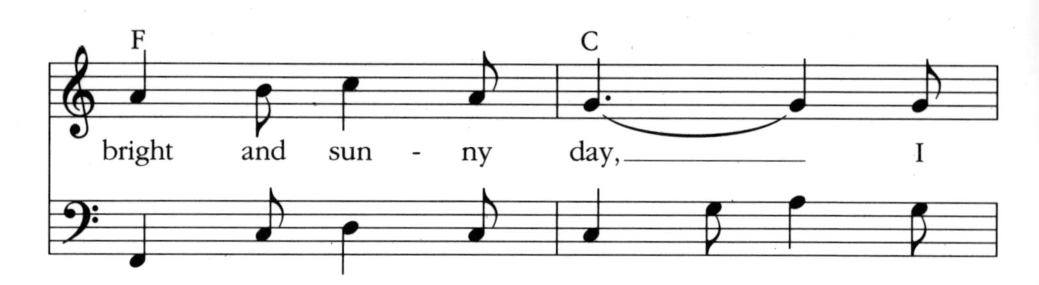

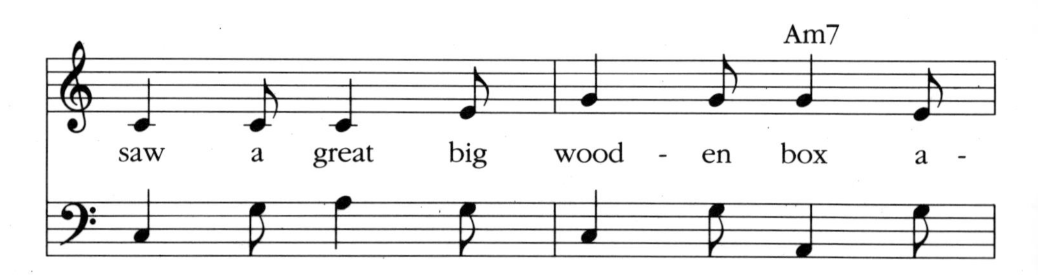

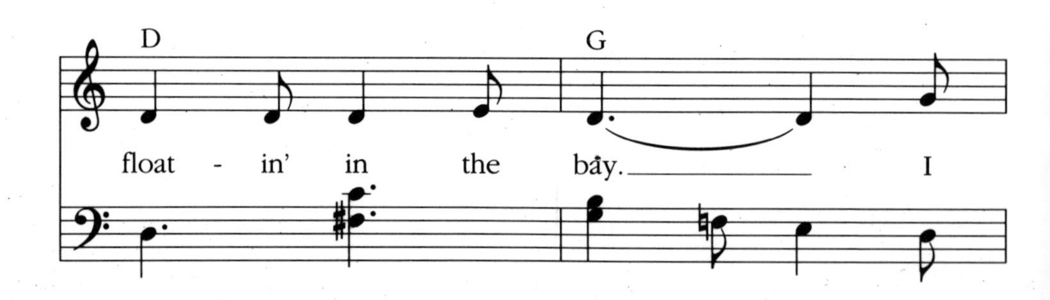

44 Frankenstein

C F D
pulled it in and o - pened it up and much to my sur -

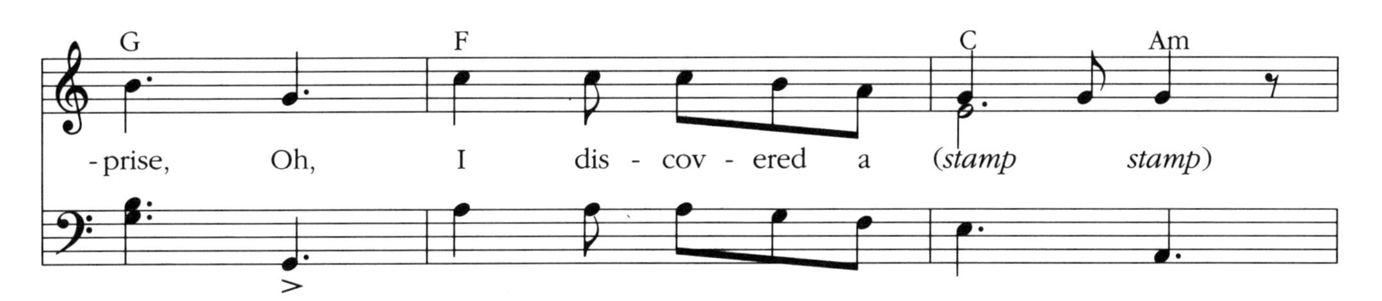

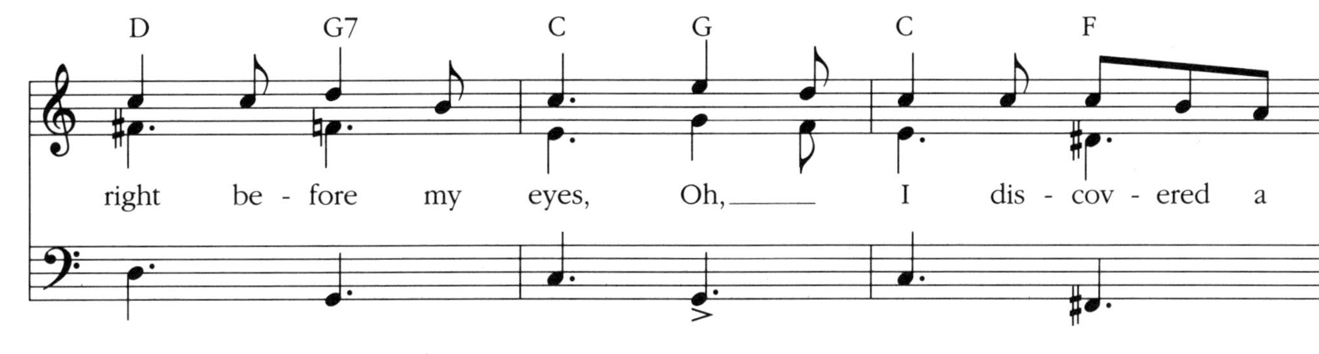

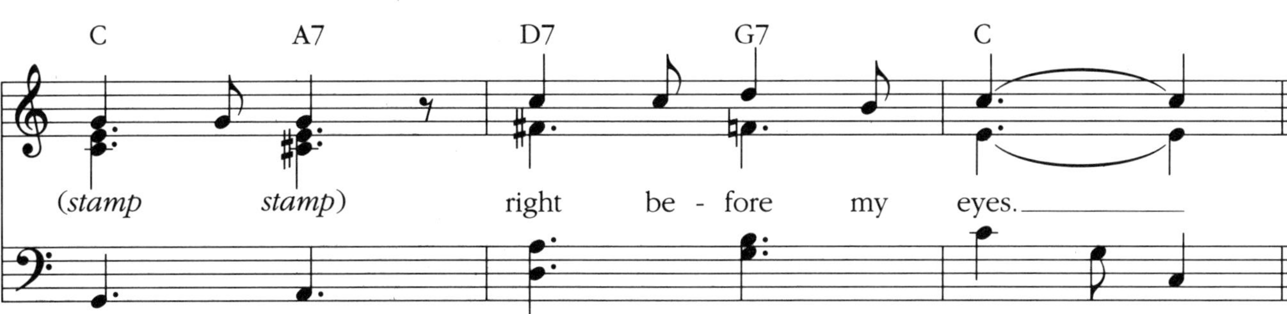

In a castle, on a mountain
Near the dark and murky Rhine,
Dwelt a doctor, the concoctor
Of the monster, Frankenstein.
  Oh my monster, oh my monster,
  Oh my monster, Frankenstein,
  You were built to last forever,
  Dreadful scary Frankenstein.

In a graveyard near the castle,
Where the moon refused to shine,
He dug for noses and for toeses
For his monster, Frankenstein.
  Oh my monster, oh my monster ...

TUNE: *Clementine*

45 Peanut butter

Traditional

There are three ways to get peanut butter off the roof of your mouth:

one way is to shake your head back and forth.

If that doesn't work, you could kind of whistle.

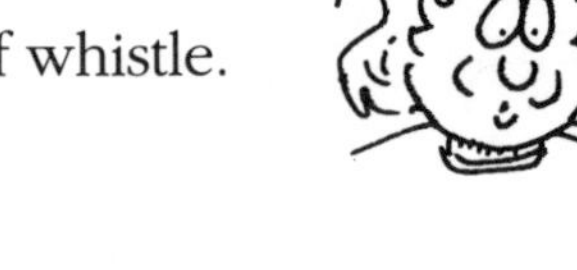

If that doesn't work, you could scrape it off
with your first finger.

There are three ways to get peanut butter off your finger.

One way is to shake it off.

Another way is to blow it off.

If that doesn't work, you can scrape it off
with your two front teeth.

There are three ways to get peanut butter off the roof of your mouth ...

46 Found a peanut

Found a peanut, found a peanut
Found a peanut last night
Last night I found a peanut
Found a peanut last night.

Cracked it open, cracked it open
Cracked it open last night
Last night I cracked it open
Cracked it open last night.

It was rotten, it was rotten ...

Ate it anyway, ate it anyway ...

Got a stomachache, got a stomachache ...

Called the doctor, called the doctor...

Appendicitis, appendicitis ...

Operation, operation ...

Died anyway, died anyway ...

Went to heaven, went to heaven ...

Met St Peter, met St Peter ...

Didn't like him, didn't like him ...

Went the other way, went the other way ...

Met the devil, met the devil ...

Shovelling coal, shovelling coal ...

Found a peanut, found a peanut ...

Cracked it open, cracked it open ...

Dramatise with actions

TUNE: *Clementine*

47 Mamma will you buy me a banana?

Traditional

Once there was a girl who was very hungry so she said:

Mamma, will you buy me a,
will you buy me a,
will you buy me a,
Mamma, will you buy me a,
will you buy me a banana.

This girl was so small she couldn't peel her own bananas so she said:

Mamma, will you peel the skin,
will you peel the skin,
will you peel the skin,
Mamma, will you peel the skin,
the skin of my banana.

This very small girl was very kind so she said:

Mamma, do you want a bite,
do you want a bite,
do you want a bite,
Mamma, do you want a bite,
a bite of my banana.

But this very small girl's mum was hungry too:

Mamma, you took too much,
you took too much,
you took too much,
Mamma, you took too much,
too much of my banana.

So this very small girl was very angry:

Mamma, you're a greedy glut,
you're a greedy glut,
you're a greedy glut,
Mamma, you're a greedy glut,
you've eaten my banana.

So there was nothing for it but to ask for another:

Mamma, will you buy me a ...

And of course the girl was so small she couldn't peel her own bananas, so she said:

Mamma, will you peel the skin ...

Now the girl did something really really silly - she said:

Mamma, do you want a bite ...

And you know what happened, don't you?

Mamma, you took too much ...

48 The lollipop song

Traditional

Oh, I'd rather suck on a lemon drop
Than try my luck with a lollipop,
'Cause a lollipop I always drop,
And it gets all over icky. *

Oh, it makes me sick the way it smears,
It gets all over my hair and ears,
With a jelly bean I'm always clean,
But a lollipop, ooh icky. *

I've tried and tried, but still I can't find
A lollipop *pop* that's halfway refined.

So I'd rather suck on a lemon drop
Than try my luck with a lollipop,
'Cause a lollipop I always drop,
And it gets all over icky. *
Ooh icky, ooh icky, icky, icky. Eugh!

***Silly sounds:** lipsmacking, slurping and **ducks**. Add them anywhere you like but particularly at* *

49 Jelly belly

Adapted from traditional by P. Trezise

Two, four, six, eight,
Tell me what is on your plate ... JELLY!
We're going to have some jelly, hurrah, hurrah!
We're going to have some jelly, hurrah, hurrah!
Jelly for your dinner, jelly for your tea,
Jelly, jelly doon your belly,
Hip, hip, hip, hurrah!

Two, four, six, eight,
Tell me what is on your plate ... ICE CREAM!
We're going to have some ice cream, hurrah, hurrah!
We're going to have some ice cream, hurrah, hurrah!
Ice cream for your dinner, ice cream for your tea,
Ice cream, jelly doon your belly,
Hip, hip, hip, hurrah!

Two, four, six, eight,
Tell me what is on your plate ... BEANS!
We're going to have some beans, hurrah, hurrah,
We're going to have some beans, hurrah, hurrah,
Beans for your dinner, beans for your tea,
Beans, ice cream, jelly doon your belly,
Hip, hip, hip, hurrah.

Two, four, six, eight,
Tell me what is on your plate ... PICKLED ONIONS!

Continue adding whatever you like to the menu.

50 Tattie soup

Traditional, collected by P. Trezise

I choket* on a tattie, a tattie,
I choket on a tattie,
A plate o' tattie, plate o'tattie,
Plate o'tattie soup.

My mother sent for the doctor, doctor,
My mother sent for the doctor,
Because of the tattie, 'cause of the tattie,
'Cause of the tattie soup.

The doctor says, 'You're dein', dein' ...

They pit me in my coffin, coffin ...

I'm in a deadee holey†, holey ...

The minister said his prayers, prayers ...

But noo I'm up in heaven, heaven ...

And the angels gave me supper, supper ...

And what did I get for my supper, supper? ...

*choked †grave

51 I had a sausage

I had a sausage, a bonny, bonny sausage,
I put it in the oven for my tea.
I went down the cellar
To get the salt and pepper,
And the sausage ran after me.

TUNE: *I love a lassie*

52 Gunerania's wedding cake

Robert Soulsby and Class 1S, Brookvale Junior School

The king he baked a wedding cake upon a sunny day,
The king he baked a wedding cake, it was in the month of May,
The king he baked a wedding cake, he filled it with old clocks,
A cabbage, and an octopus, some apples and red socks.
He mixed it, he whisked it, he threw it on the floor,
He crushed it, he mushed it, and it slithered out the door.

The king he baked a wedding cake and the glue he used was runny,
The king he baked a wedding cake with spiders and some honey,
The king he baked a wedding cake, he filled it with rusty nails,
A crocodile, a felt-tip pen, and a pinch of powdered snails.
He folded it, he moulded it, he squeezed it through his toes,
He sliced it, and diced it, 'til the flour went up his nose.

The king he baked a wedding cake, he added ripe bananas,
The king he baked a wedding cake, it was striped like his pyjamas,
The king he baked a wedding cake, it was sixty-one feet high,
It weighed ten tons, it squashed his thumbs, which made the poor king cry.
He iced it, he sliced it, he packed it with black slugs,
He covered it in manky moss, and a crust of orange bugs.

The king he baked a wedding cake with rats and cats and bats,
The king he baked a wedding cake with a thousand buzzing gnats,
The king he baked a wedding cake he gave it to the queen,
It made her sick for fifty years and turned her blue and green.
She bashed him, she thrashed him, she hit him with a frog,
She swung him, she flung him, and slapped him with a log.

53 I can't do my bally bottom button up

Words and music: J. P. Long

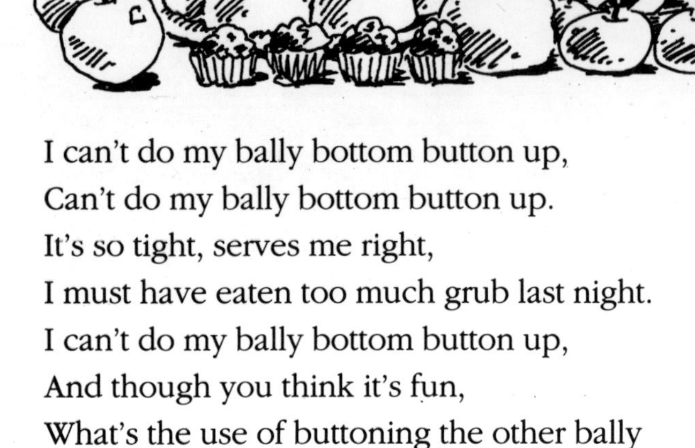

I can't do my bally bottom button up,
Can't do my bally bottom button up.
It's so tight, serves me right,
I must have eaten too much grub last night.
I can't do my bally bottom button up,
And though you think it's fun,
What's the use of buttoning the other bally
buttons,
When the bally bottom button's undone?

54 TV dinners

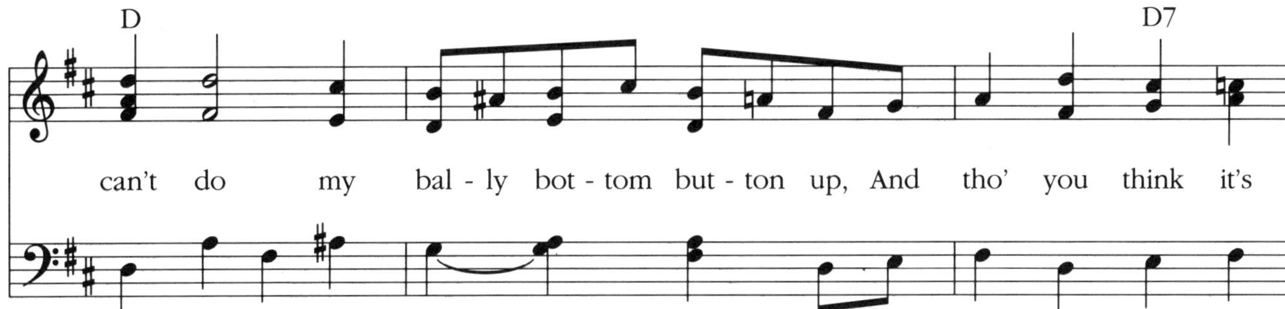

How does Batman's mother call him in for tea?

Dinner, dinner, dinner, dinner,
Dinner, dinner, dinner, dinner, Batman!

(*Sing to* Batman *theme tune*)

How does the Pink Panther chase insects?

Dead ant, dead ant, dead ant, dead ant,
dead ant ...

(Pink Panther *theme tune*)

How does Bob Marley like his doughnuts?

Wi' jam in, jam in, and I hope you like
jam in too.

(Jamming)

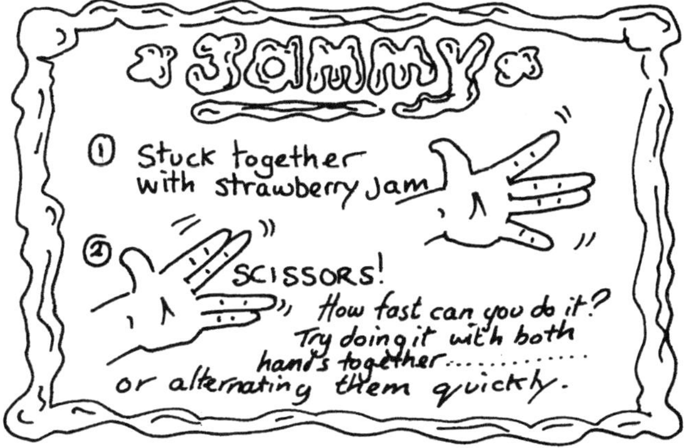

55 Over the garden wall

Traditional

Over the garden wall
I let my baby fall.
My mother came out,
She gave me a clout,
Over the garden wall.

Over the garden wall
I let my baby fall.
My mother came out,
She gave me a clout,
She asked me what it was all about,
Over the garden wall.

Over the garden wall
I let my baby fall,
My mother came out,
She gave me a clout,
She gave me another to match the other,
She asked me what it was all about,
Over the garden wall.

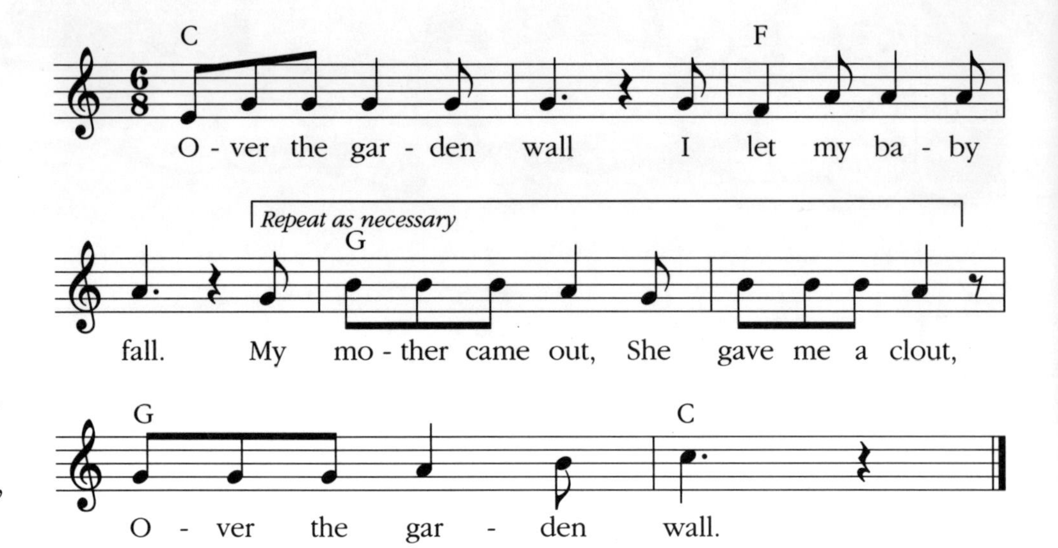

56 When I was a wee wee tot

Traditional

When I was a wee wee tot,
They took me from my wee wee cot,
They put me on my wee wee pot
To see if I would wee or not.

When they found that I would not,
They took me from my wee wee pot,
They put me in my wee wee cot,
Where I wee wee quite a lot.

***Silly sounds:** one group can do **baby burblers** throughout as an accompaniment.*

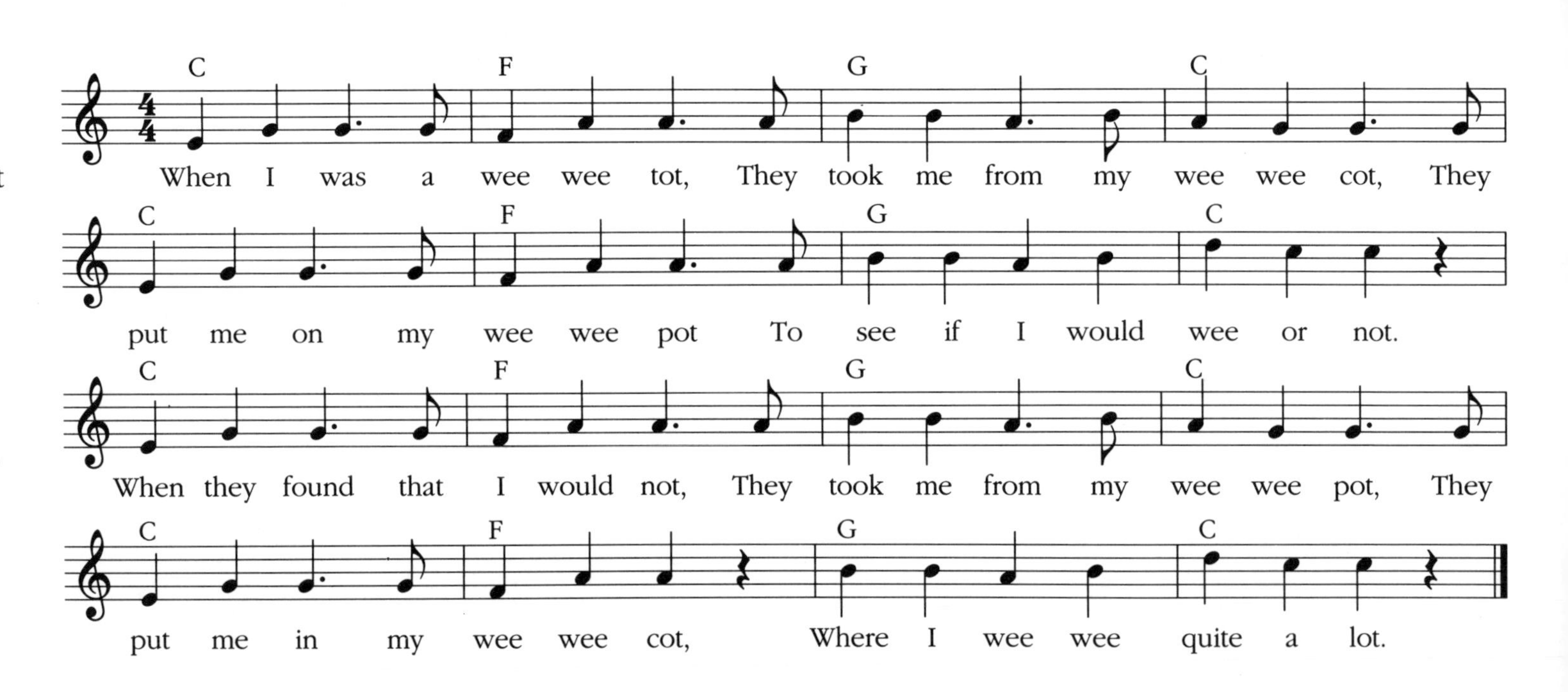

57 Sylvest

Traditional, collected by Michael Rosen

He's my big brother Sylvest.
WHAT'S HE GOT?
He's got a row of forty medals 'cross his chest.
BIG CHEST!
Don't push, don't shove, plenty of room for
you and me.
He's got an arm like a leg. BIG LEG!
And a punch that'd sink a battleship,
BIG SHIP!
Takes all the army and the navy
To put the wind up
SYLVEST!

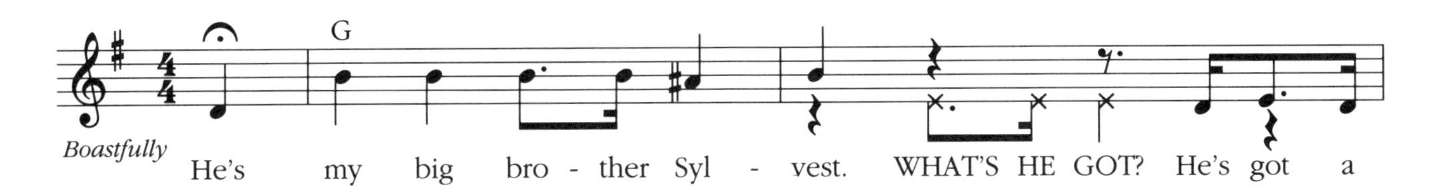

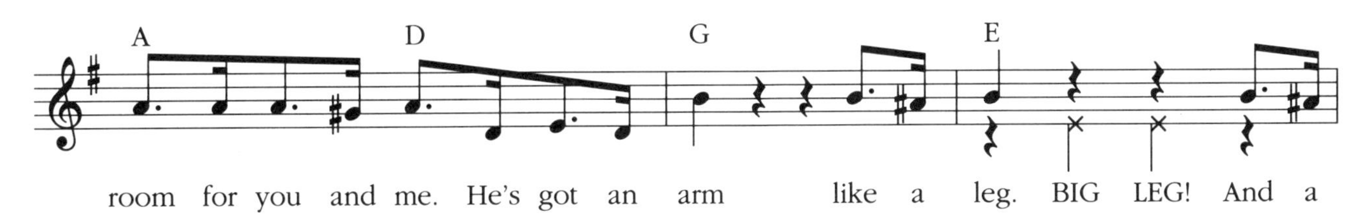

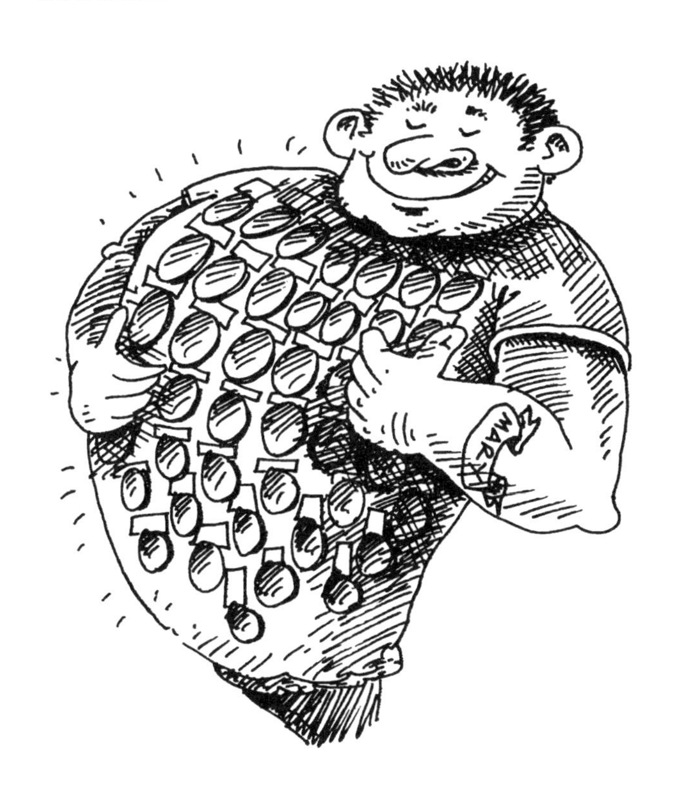

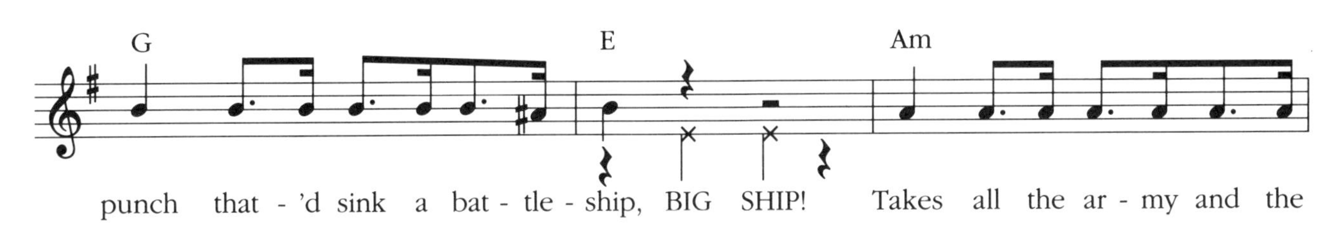

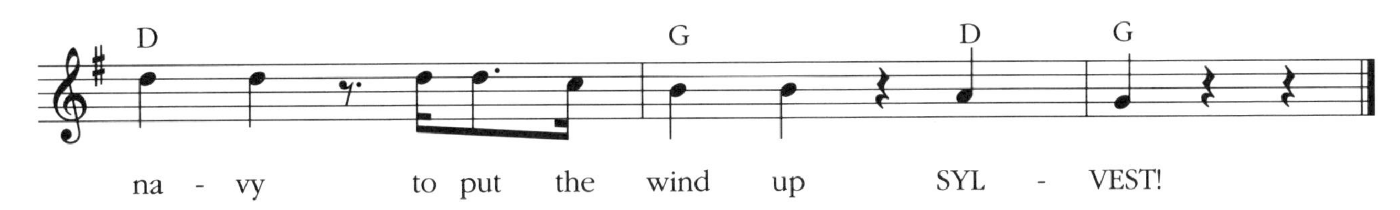

58 Down came the rain

Words: Robin Conrad *Music: Mitch Murray*

She walked like a dream from another world,
I'd never seen such a lovely girl.
She smiled as we stood on the sand,
But just as I reached for her hand –
  DOWN CAME THE RAIN,
  It's happened again,
  The thunder and lightning,
  DOWN CAME THE RAIN.

We walked by the sea for a long long time,
I knew somehow she was nearly mine;
The look in her eyes told me this,
But just as we stopped for a kiss:
  DOWN CAME THE RAIN ...

She whispered to me she would be my bride,
She'd always be standing by my side;
I'd come to the end of my search;
But just as we came to the church:
  DOWN CAME THE RAIN,
  It's happened again,
  The thunder and lightning,
  DOWN CAME THE RAIN,
  DOWN CAME THE RAIN,
  DOWN CAME THE RAIN.

G7
C7
F
Dm7
just as I reached for her hand –
ff
DOWN CAME THE RAIN,
Furiously
Gm7
C
F
Dm7
Gm7
C
F
Dm7
it's hap - pened a - gain,
The thun - der and light - ning,
Gm7
C7
1. 2.
F
Dm7
B♭
C7
D.S.
3.
F
Dm7
DOWN CAME THE RAIN.
We
RAIN,
Gm
C7
F
Dm
Gm7
C7
F
(A♭
B♭)
F
DOWN CAME THE RAIN,
DOWN CAME THE RAIN.
rall e cresc.
ff

59 Lord Jim

Traditional

I know an old bloke and his name is Lord Jim,
And he had a wife who threw tomatoes at him,
Now tomatoes are juicy, don't injure the skin,
But these ones they did, they was inside a tin.
  Ho-je-ra, what d'you say?
  For the queen of society lives down our way.

I know an old lady, her name is Miss Brown,
She was having a bath and she couldn't come down,
She said that she would be down in a tick,
She slipped on the soap and she did come down quick.
  Ho-je-ra, what d'you say?
  For the queen of society lives down our way.

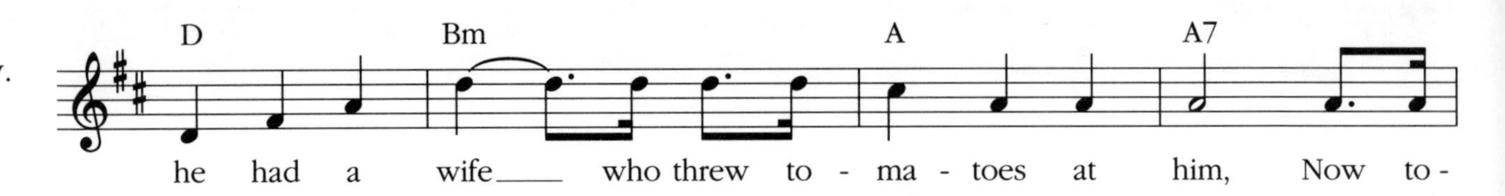

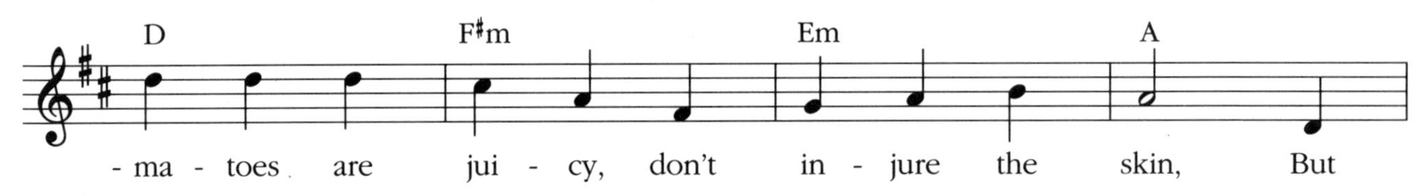

60 Checkmate

King George, he had a date,
He stayed out very late,
He was the King.
Queen Mary paced the floor,
King George came home at four,
She met him at the door -
God save the King.

TUNE: *God save the King/Queen*

61 'Itched up

The mosquitoes wore tuxedoes
and the blackflies wore black ties,
The bride she was a spider
and the groom he was a snake,
They were going to a wedding
in my Aunt Lucy's bedding,
And she was the wedding cake.

Glory, glory, hallelujah,
You don't feel itchy, Aunty, do ya?
Glory, glory, hallelujah,
The bugs marched down the aisle.

The little honeymooners
were nice and cozy in her bloomers,
And the guests all took their places
in Aunt Lucy's pillowcases.
The little beasts had such a feast,
they danced and flew and soared,
All while Aunt Lucy snored.
Glory, glory hallelujah ...

TUNE: *John Brown's body*

62 Stitched up

Granny's in the kitchen
Doing a bit of stitching,
In came a bogie man and chased granny out -
BOO!
'Well,' said Granny, 'That's not fair!'
'Well,' said the bogie man, 'I don't care!'

Traditional chant

63 Washed up

Oh, the Yellow Rose of Texas
And the man from Laramie
Invited Davey Crockett to have a cup of tea.
The tea was so delicious they had another cup
And left poor Davey Crockett to do the
washing up.

TUNE: *The Yellow Rose of Texas*

64 Socked

While shepherds washed their socks by night,
While watching ITV,
The Angel of the Lord came down
And switched to BBC.

TUNE: *While shepherds watched their flocks*

65 Undressed

We're walking through the air,
I've lost my underwear,
I'm going to Mothercare
to buy another pair
to wear ...

TUNE: *We're walking in the air*

66 Hi! my name's Joe

Traditional

Hi! my name's Joe,
And I work in a button fact'ry,
Got a wife, one kid.
One day the boss said,
'Joe, are you busy?'
I said, 'No.' So he said,
'Push the button with your right hand.'
choo choo choo choo choo

Hi! my name's Joe
And I work in a button fact'ry,
Got a wife, two kids.
One day the boss said,
'Joe, are you busy?'
I said, 'No.' So he said,
'Push the button with your left hand.'
choo choo choo choo choo

Carry on adding more kids and more bits of your body - left leg, right leg, bum, head - then:

'Hi! my name's Joe,
And I work in a button fact'ry,
Got a wife, seven kids.
One day the boss said,
'Joe, are you busy?'
And I said, 'YEEEEEEEEEEEEEEEESSSS!'

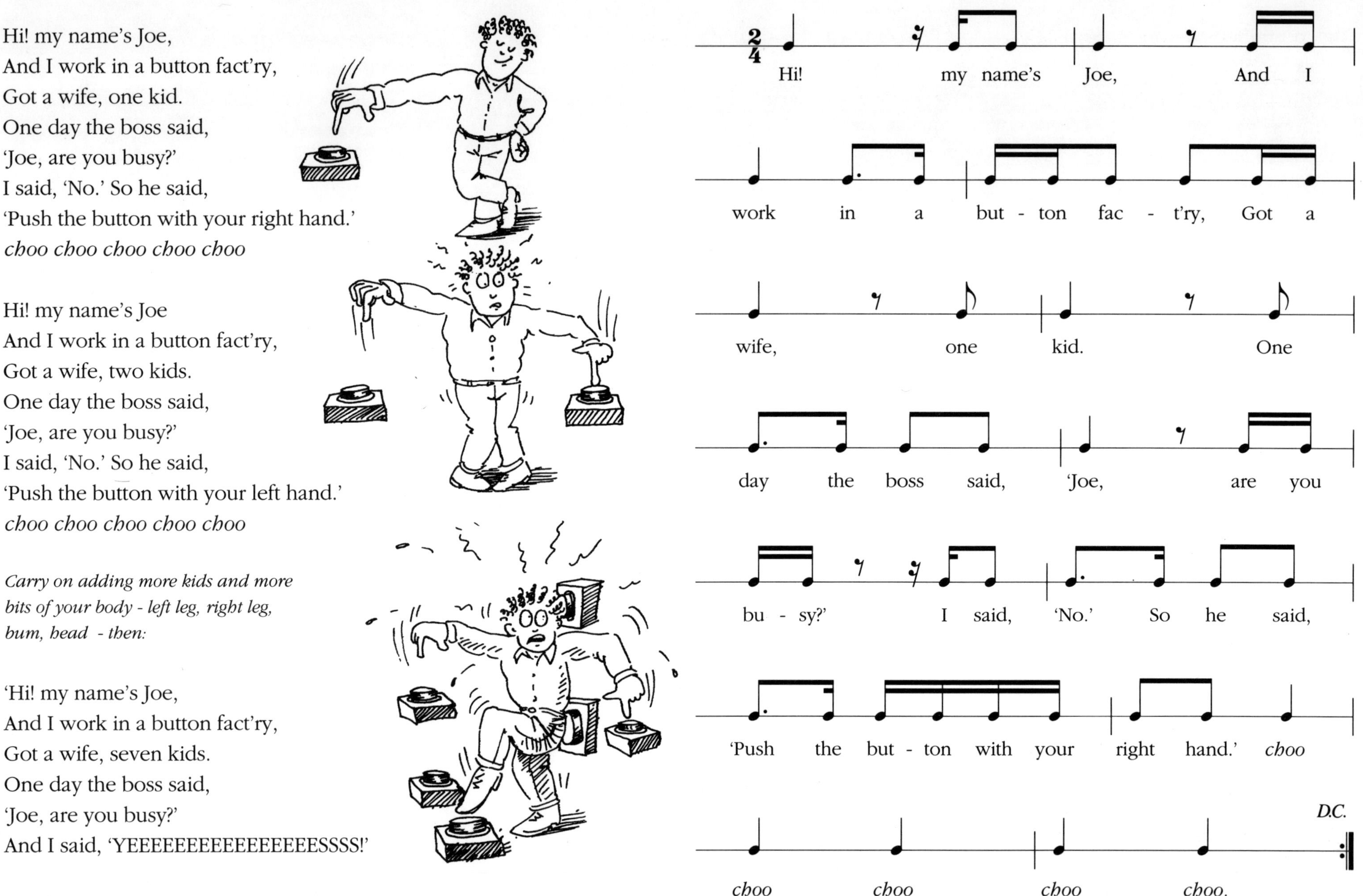

67 Oh, ye canny shove yer granny aff a bus

Adapted from traditional by P. Trezise for The Singing Kettle

Oh, ye canny shove yer granny aff a bus, push push,
Oh, ye canny shove yer granny aff a bus, push push,
Oh, ye canny shove yer granny, cause she's yer mammy's mammy,
Oh, ye canny shove yer granny aff a bus, push push.

Oh, we'll all go round to see her after school, hello granny,
Oh, we'll all go round to see her after school, hello granny,
Oh, we'll all go round to see her, all go round to see her,
Oh, we'll all go round to see her after school, hello granny, push push.

Oh, she'll gie us mince and tatties when we go, yum yum …
Oh, she'll gie us mince and tatties when we go, yum yum, hello granny, push push.

Oh, ye canny eat yer porridge wi' a fork, slurp slurp …
Oh, ye canny eat yer porridge wi' a fork, slurp slurp, yum yum, hello granny, push push.

Oh, my granny wears an awfee woolly vest, scratch scratch,
Oh, my granny wears an awfee woolly vest, scratch scratch,
Oh, my granny wears a vest, an awfee woolly vest,
Oh, my granny wears an awfee woolly vest, scratch scratch, slurp slurp, yum yum, hello granny, push push.

Oh, ye canny shove yer granny aff a bus, aye ye can …
Oh, ye canny shove yer granny aff a bus, aye ye can, scratch scratch, slurp slurp, yum yum, hello granny, push push.

68 Flash bang wallop

Words and music: David Heneker

All lined up in a wedding group,
Here we are for a photograph.
We're all dressed up in a morning suit,
All trying not to laugh,
Since the early caveman in his fur
Took a trip to Gretna Green,
There's always been a photographer
To record the happy scene.

Hold it, flash, bang, wallop, what a picture,
Click, what a picture what a photograph.
Poor old bloke, blimey what a joke,
Hat blown off in a cloud of smoke.
Clap hands, *clap clap clap clap*
Stamp your feet, *stamp stamp*
Bang it on the big bass drum, *boing*
What a picture, what a picture,
Rum tiddely um pum, pum, pum, pum.
Stick it in your family album.

You've read it in the Folio
Or seen the Shakespeare play,
How Juliet fell for Romeo,
In the merry month of May.
And as he climbed the orchard wall
To reach his lady fair,
As he tumbled she began to bawl
As he travelled through the air –

Hold it, flash, bang, wallop, what a picture,
Click, what a picture what a photograph.
Poor old bloke, didn't see the joke,
Tights all torn and his doublets broke,
Clap hands, *clap clap clap clap*
Stamp your feet, *stamp stamp*
Bang it on the big bass drum – *boing*
What a picture, what a picture,
Rum tiddely um pum, pum, pum, pum.
Stick it in your family album.

When Napoleon married Josephine,
There was just the same to-do,
He galloped home from the battle-scene,
All the way from Waterloo,
And as he came straight from off his horse
To the boudoir where she sat,
She said to him - in French, of course -
As he took off his big cocked hat:

Hold it, flash, bang, wallop, what a picture,
Click, what a picture, what a photograph.
There she was leaning on the bar.
Pink champagne - oo la la!
Clap hands, *clap clap clap clap*
Stamp your feet, *stamp stamp*
Bang it on the big bass drum - *boing*
What a picture, what a picture,
Rum tiddely um pum, pum, pum, pum.
Stick it in your family album.

69 'Neath the crust of the old apple pie

Traditional North American

'Neath the crust of the old apple pie
There is something for you and for I;
It may be a pin that the cook has dropped in,
Or it may be a dear little fly, (dear little fly).
It may be an old rusty nail,
Or a piece of dear puppy dog's tail,
But whatever it be, it's for you and for me,
'Neath the crust of the old apple pie.

(Repeat)

D

may be an old rust - y nail, Or a

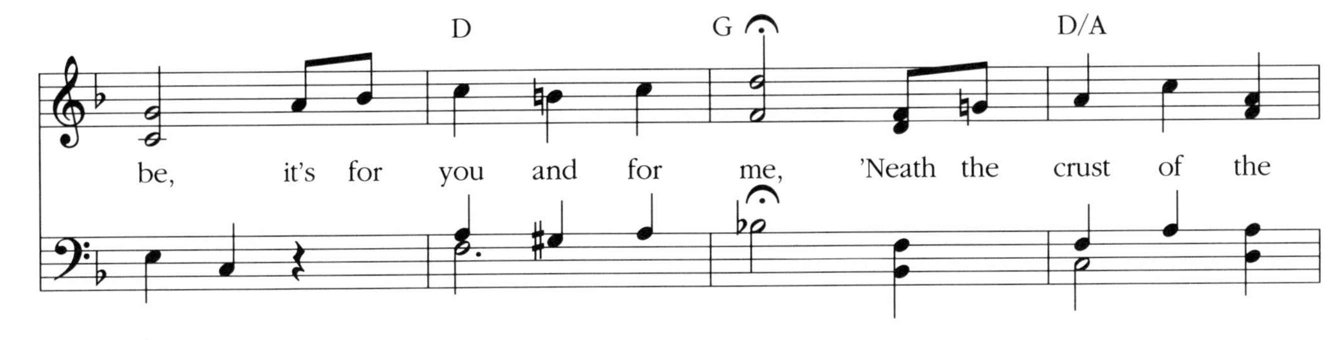

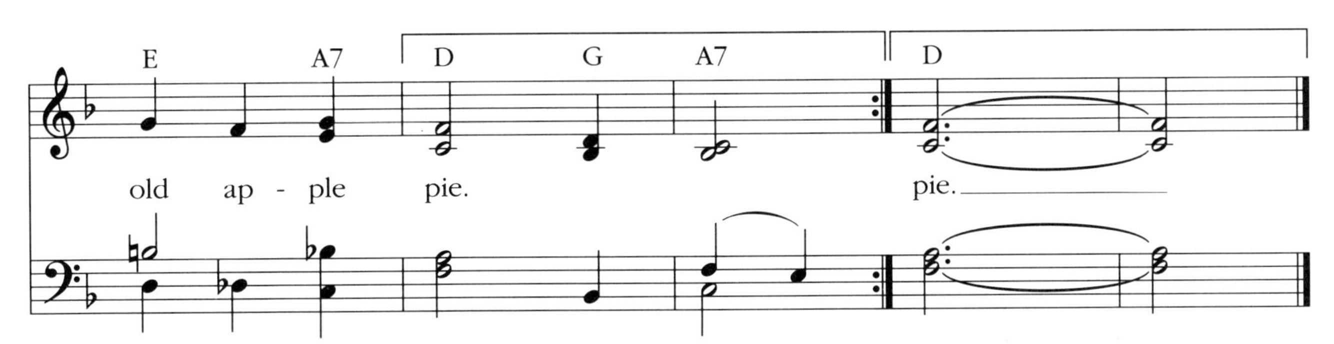

70 Quick, quick

Quick, quick,
The cat's been sick,
Where, where,
Under the stair,
Hasten, hasten,
Fetch a basin,
Alas alack, 'tis all in vain,
Pussy's eaten it up again.

Traditional

71 School dinners

School dinners,
School dinners,
Iron beans,
Iron beans,
Sloppy semolina,
Sloppy semolina,
I feel sick,
Get a bowl quick.

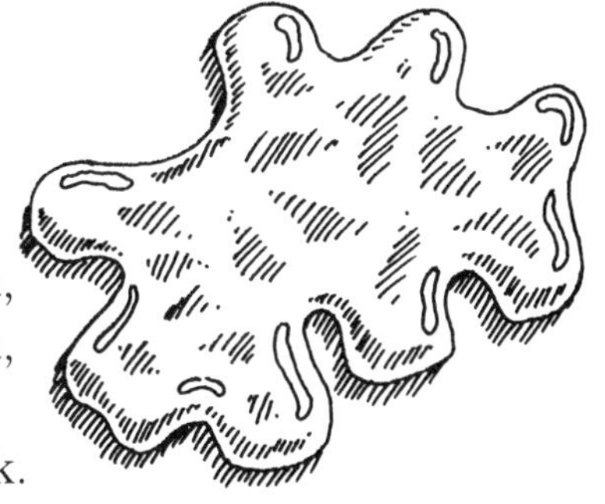

TUNE: *Frère Jacques*

72 Black socks

Traditional

Black socks, they never get dirty,
The longer you wear them the stronger they get.
Sometimes I think I should wash them,
But something inside me keeps saying,
'Not yet, not yet, not yet, not yet, not yet.'

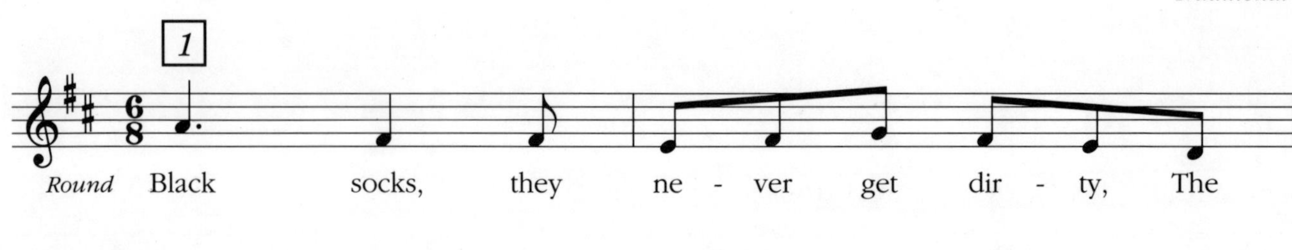

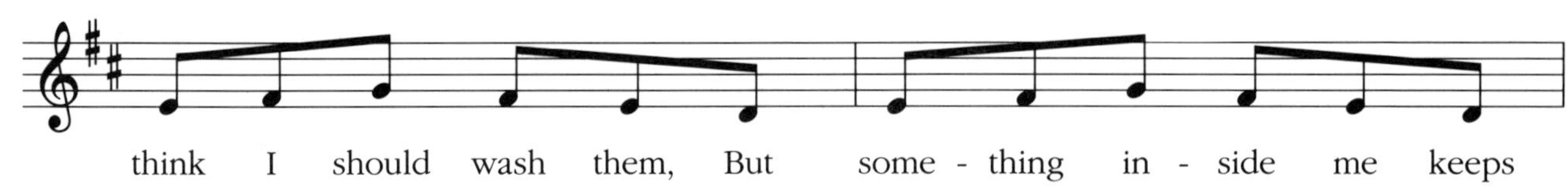

73 Everybody's doing it

Everybody's doing it, doing it, doing it,
Picking their nose and chewing it, chewing it, chewing it.
Rolling it up and flicking it, flicking it, flicking it …

TUNE: *Everybody do this*

74 Nobody loves me

Traditional

Nobody loves me, everybody hates me,
Guess I'll go and eat worms,
Long slim slimy ones, short fat juicy ones,
Itsy bitsy fuzzy wuzzy worms.

First you cut the heads off, then you suck the guts out
Oh, how they wiggle and squirm,
Long slim slimy ones, short fat juicy ones,
Itsy bitsy fuzzy wuzzy worms.

Wiggle goes the first one, goosh goes the second one,
Sure don't wanna eat these worms,
Long slim slimy ones, short fat juicy ones,
Itsy bitsy fuzzy wuzzy worms.

Down goes the first one, down goes the second one
Sure hate the taste of worms,
Long slim slimy ones, short fat juicy ones,
Itsy bitsy fuzzy wuzzy worms.

Nobody hates me, everybody likes me,
Never should've eaten those worms,
Long slim slimy ones, short fat juicy ones,
Itsy bitsy fuzzy wuzzy worms.

Up comes the first one, up comes the second one,
Oh, how they wiggle and squirm,
Long slim slimy ones, short fat juicy ones,
Itsy bitsy fuzzy wuzzy worms.

75 Dunderbeck

Traditional

Oh once there was a butcher,
his name was Dunderbeck,
He made such tasty sausages
that no one would suspect –
Whatever chanced to pass in reach
of Dunderbeck's machine,
Would flavour the butcher's sausages
and never more be seen.

Oh Dunderbeck, oh Dunderbeck,
how could you be so mean,
To ever have invented the
sausage meat machine?
Now long-tailed rats and pussy-cats,
scrawny, fat and lean,
They'll all be ground to sausage meat
in Dunderbeck's machine.

One sunny day a little boy
came walking in the store,
He bought a pound of sausages
and made towards the door,
Then he began to whistle,
he whistled up a tune,
The sausages, they jumped, they barked,
they danced around the room.

Today the thing got busted,
the darn thing wouldn't go,
And Dunderbeck he crawled inside
to see what made it so.
His wife came walking in just then,
from shopping in the street,
She brushed against the starting rod
and Dunderbeck was meat! Bang!

76 I love to do my homework

Traditional

I love to do my homework,
it makes me feel so good,
I love to do exactly as the teacher
says I should.
I love to do my schoolwork,
I love it ev'ry day,
And I also love these men in white
who are taking me away.

77 Oh, my old man's a dustman

Traditional

Oh, my old man's a dustman,
He wears a dustman's hat,
He bought two thousand tickets
To see a football match.

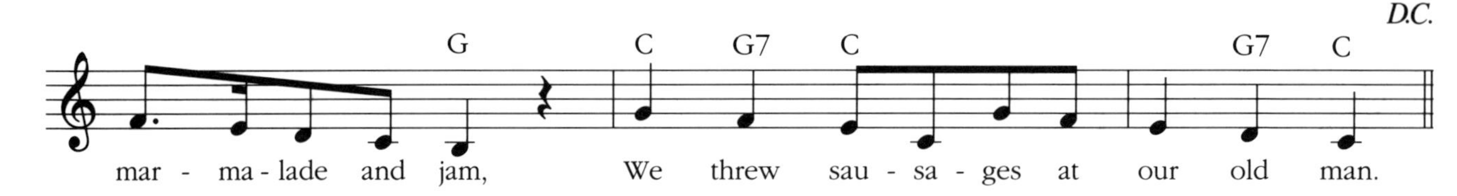

Oh, Fatty passed to Skinny
And Skinny passed it back,
Fatty took a rotten shot
And knocked the goalie flat, OOH!

Where was the goalie,
When the ball was in the net?

Half way up the goalpost
With his trousers round his neck. Singing:

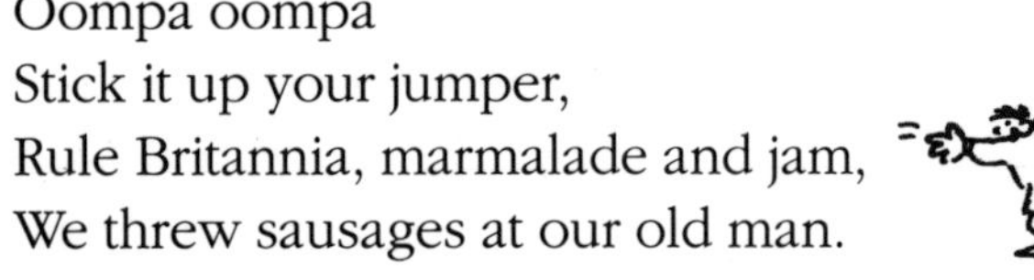

Oompa oompa
Stick it up your jumper,
Rule Britannia, marmalade and jam,
We threw sausages at our old man.

They put him on the stretcher,
They put him on the bed,
They rubbed his belly with a five pound jelly,
But the poor old soul was dead.

78 Ellery my son

Where have you been all the day,
Ellery my son?
Where have you been all the day,
my beloved one?

In the woods, mother,
in the woods, mother,
Oh, mother, come quick,
I wanna be sick,
and lay me down to die.

What were you doing in the woods,
Ellery my son?
What were you doing in the woods,
my sugar plum?

Eating, mother, eating, mother ...

What were you eating in the woods ...
my currant bun?

Eels, mother, eels, mother ...

What colour were these eels ... my darling one?

Green and yellow, green and yellow ...

They weren't eels, they must have
been snakes ... my honey bun!

Eugh, mother, eugh, mother,
Oh, mother come quick,
oh, mother come quick,
I think that I am DEAD!

Traditional

79 Plainsy R.I.P.

Traditional, collected by Susanna Steele

Plainsy had an aunty, an aunty very poor,
One day she said to Plainsy, 'Get down and scrub the floor.'
Plainsy didn't like it, he went upstairs to bed,
Fell right down the bannister and landed on his head. BANG.
 More work for the undertaker,
 'Nother little job for the tombstone maker,
 In the local cemetery,
 On a tombstone you will see
 Plainsy - R.I.P.

Plainsy went to the station without a hat or coat,
Went sliding down the railway track on a bar of Sunlight Soap.
Along came a runaway engine right on Plainsy's track,
And would you believe, he rolled up his sleeves, and he pushed that engine back. BANG.
 More work for the undertaker ...

Plainsy had an uncle, an uncle very rich,
One day he said to Plainsy, 'I'll give you two and six.'
Plainsy took the money, he went down to the shop.
Ten lemonades and ten ginger beers, and Plainsy went off POP. BANG!
 More work for the undertaker ...

80 The worms crawl in, the worms crawl out

Traditional

Whenever you see a hearse go by,
Oooh ah, oooh ah,
Remember, one day *you've* got to die,
Oooh ah, oooh ah.

They wrap you up in a clean white sheet,
Oooh ah, oooh ah,
And drop your box down thirteen feet.
Oooh ah, oooh ah.

All goes well for about a week ...
And then the coffin begins to leak ...

Your eyes fall in and your teeth fall out ...
And maggots play ping-pong on your snout ...

Your fingers rot, and so do your toes ...
Your brains come tumbling down your nose ...

After a while your face turns green ...
And pus pours out like clotted cream ...

The worms crawl in, the worms crawl out ...
They go in thin and they come out stout ...

So whenever you see a hearse go by,
Oooh ah, oooh ah,
Remember one day, *you've* got to die,
Oooh ah, oooh ah,
How happy we shall be.

Silly sounds

Aeroplane— drone an *oo* sound, then start to whistle at the same time. Try going up and down.

Baby burblers— push lips forward, say *boo*, and flap lips with one finger.

Bagpiper— hold nose with one hand and sing a Scottish tune to the syllables *nyah-ee-yah-ee-nyah*. With the side of the other hand, quickly and lightly chop your adam's apple.

Beatbox— cup mouth with hands and make up a typical pop rhythm out of mouth sounds - use lip raspberries (as if blowing a trumpet) interrupted by percussive sounds made with the consonants *ch*, *k*, and *ch* (as in *loch*).

Bodyscratcher— scratch all over with one hand, while the other secretly scratches the underside of a table or chair.

Cheekpoppers— either put your finger in the side of your mouth and pop it out, or form an *o* with your lips, and flick your cheek.

Ducks— roll tongue backwards on to the roof of your mouth and suck.

Groundshaker— grit teeth, put tongue flat against the roof of your mouth and blow air out between your back teeth and your cheeks. Shake your head so that your cheeks flap, or pinch and flap them with your fingers. Precede all this with a slowly descending whistle.

Headbopper— tap head with knuckles of one hand while secretly banging the underside of a table or chair with the other.

Spineshivers— stretch a blade of grass side on between your thumbs and blow through them.

Underarm squelch— cup your hand over your armpit. Bring your arm down hard onto your hand to make a raspberry sound.

Acknowledgements

The following have kindly granted their permission for the reprinting of copyright words and music:

Anthea Askey and Will Fyffe Jnr for **I'm a little wrong note** by Arthur Askey.

Morag Blance for **Nell and Ned**, runner up in the A & C Black Silly Song Competition.

Sheetal Borhara, Trina Bose, Sara Isenberg, Martina Klich and Rebecca Ryan of Moss Hall Junior School for **Are you pink and green?** highly commended in the A & C Black Silly Song Competition.

Bushranger/Bark Music for **Star trekkin'** by Grahame Lister, John O'Conner and R. Kehoe.

Campbell Connelly & Co., Ltd for **The biggest aspidistra in the world** by Jimmy Harper, Will Haines and Tommie Connor, © 1938 Campbell Connelly and Co Ltd, 8-9 Frith Street, London W1V 5TZ, and for **Down came the rain**, music by Mitch Murray, words by Robin Conrad, © 1965, by Clan Music/Shapiro Bernstein and Co Ltd.

Essex Music for **The Thing** by Charles R. Grean, © 1950 (renewed) by Grean Music for the USA: administered for the USA by September Music Inc. Sub-published by Tro Music Ltd, Suite 207, Plaza 535 Kings Road, London SW10 0SZ. International copyright secured. All rights reserved. Used by permission.

Peter Gosling for the music to **Jibber jabber**, © Peter Gosling 1991.

International Music Publications Limited, Southend Road, Woodford Green, Essex 1G8 8HN, for: **A G-nu**, words by Michael Flanders, music by Michael Flanders and Donald Swann, © 1974 Chappell Music Ltd, London W1Y 3FA/International Music Publications Limited; **Flash bang wallop**, words and music by David Heneker, © 1963 Chappell Music Ltd/International Music Publications Limited; **The flies crawled up the window**, words by Douglas Furber, music by Vivian Ellis, © 1933 Chappell Music Ltd, London W1Y 3FA/ International Music Publications Limited; **I can't do my bally bottom button up**, words and music by J. P. Long, © 1916 Star Music Publishing, B. Feldman & Co Ltd, London WC2H 0EA; **Purple People Eater** by Sheb Wooley, © 1958 Channel Music Co, USA, Peter Maurice Music Co. Ltd, London WC2H 0EA; **The Court of King Caractacus** by Rolf Harris, © 1964 Ardmore & Beechwood Ltd, trading as Black Swan Ltd, London WC2H 0EA. All titles used by permission

Hal Shaper Ltd for **High Hopes** by Sammy Cahn and James Van Heusen © 1959 Maraville Music Corporation.

The Singing Kettle for **Jelly belly**, **Oh ye canny shove yer granny aff a bus** and **A poor old man**, trad/Mackintosh © Kettle Music; and for their help in providing the source of **Apples and bananas**, **Says she to me** and **Tattie Soup**.

Robert Soulsby and Class 1S, Brookvale Junior School for **Generania's Wedding Cake**, first prize winner in the A & C Black Silly Song Competition.

Kaye Umansky for **Nobody nose**. Used by kind permission of Kaye Umansky, c/o Caroline Sheldon Literary Agency, © 1992.

Every effort has been made to trace and acknowledge copyright owners. If any right has been omitted, the publishers offer their apologies and will rectify this in subsequent editions following notification.

The author and publishers would also like to thank the following:

Bill Cubin and the Laurel & Hardy Museum, Ulverston, Cumbria, for the directions for **Earsy Kneesy Nosey**.
Paula Chateauneuf, Nancy Kerr and Susanna Steele for contributing traditional material.
Barrie Carson Turner for the piano accompaniments to numbers 15, 18, 27, 29, 32, 69.
Tim Roberts for the piano accompaniment to number 39.
Jane Sebba for the piano accompaniments to numbers 11, 28, 30, 31, 37, 42, 43, 48, 58, 74, 75, 76, 78.

The title, **Sonsense Nongs**, was suggested by Josie Cohen as part of the A & C Black Silly Song Competition.